SLURRY
&
STRAWBERRIES

by

Carol Hathorne

MEMORIES
of a
TIPTON CHILDHOOD

The Black Country Society

First Impression September 2002

ISBN 0 904015 68 8

Prepared for publication by Stan Hill, former Editor of *The Blackcountryman*

Cover design by the Charles Group, Kingswinford DY6 8AW
incorporating David Barlow's Illustrations.

Printed by Waterloo Design & Print plc *(incorporating Reliance Printing Works),*
Birmingham Street, Halesowen B63 3HW

In memory of Eliza Sheldon.

20.10.1918 - 8.6.1987

'.... *vigorously scrubbing*'.

ONE

Big Aunt Ginny pulled your teeth out. I tried not to remember how she'd done it to me, as I watched her, vigorously scrubbing my little brother's hot and dirty face with a soap dampened corner of her apron.

'Keep still, yer little bugger!' The 'clank-clank' of her wedding ring against his open mouth was drowned as he gasped and squirmed and finally began to bellow his protests.

'Aaargh! That hurts! I'll tell me Mom!'

Big Aunt Ginny's long, gaunt face scowled. She didn't answer, but her grip tightened on Dave's flailing arms, effectively pinning him down onto the scrubbed top table as she grimly applied the green 'Sunlight' and cold water.

Standing forgotten by the back door, I trembled in the atmosphere of tension and danger that always came descending, when our mother went away.

Big Aunt Ginny didn't like us. I knew it with a deep, eight year old's instinctive certainty. It was because she didn't like us that she used her wedding ring as a face scraper, and her long, strong fingers as pliers to pull out our baby teeth.

She had five children of her own in her cramped council house in the Lost City estate in Tipton where we all lived. With fires to light and a range to black lead, plus chickens in the back yard and a husband who, by all accounts, had once left her to start another family with a woman in Shropshire, she had her hands full. In addition, her aged mother and dependant older sister, both lived next door to her, with us.

The last thing Big Aunt Ginny needed was to have to take care of us while our mother went to work, and our dad was in the hospital!

How long our dad was in the hospital for I didn't know, and I turned away to think about it while Aunt Ginny relentlessly scrubbed my brother's nose. Any minute now, she'd discover his first ever loose 'tootsie peg' as she droolingly called them, and all hell would break loose!

I remembered being at Nan's, about two miles away, in Walker Street. While Dave and I played in the garden and Nan and Mom busied themselves in the small kitchen extension grandly called 'the verandah', Dad roared off on his motor bike to go for a lunch time drink.

When he had the crash, they found a bag of sweets in his pocket and whenever I thought of them, I felt a rush of guilt. It must have been our fault, mine and Dave's, that the accident happened, because on his way back from the 'Golden Cup' Dad had stopped to buy us dolly mixtures.

Anyway, there he was now, in Dudley Guest hospital, and we weren't allowed to see him. He had, as my Nan gravely told everybody, something called a 'fractured femur.' It sounded very grand and serious, and the impact of it had changed our lives.

Now, Mom went out to work, and because it was school holidays and Granny Coley and Aunt Maud were too old to take care of us, we had to spend our days with Big Aunt Ginny.

Gone were the delights of coming sleepily downstairs in the morning to cups of sweet, milky tea, and butter, spread on soft white bread from the baker's man, and melted under the grill . Instead, we were bundled next door to share in a much less leisurely breakfast of puffed wheat, where there was never enough to go round, while Mom dashed off to catch her bus to the factory.

Gone too, was the prospect of going out to play in the street or the outlying waste ground we called 'the fields', because Big Aunt Ginny took her responsibilities seriously, and was full of warnings about the nearby 'cut'. We might be a nuisance, but she was determined to keep her eye on us!

'Car -rul!' As my brother escaped triumphantly from under her arm, his tooth miraculously undetected, Aunt Ginny looked round for her next victim. 'Cum on, let's get that tidemark off yer neck!'

Panic stricken, I caught at my breath. Even though I no longer had any loose teeth for her to operate on, being in Aunt Ginny's grasp was still a fate worse than death.

Just as the big woman bore down on me, however, there came the sound of the side gate banging, and my eldest cousin, Brenda came in, tired and grimy, from the factory.

'Yer mother's comin'!' she said offhandedly in my direction, as she walked into the cluttered back kitchen, and without waiting for a reply: 'Any tay in that pot, our Mother? I'm spittin' feathers!'

As Big Aunt Ginny turned to the gas stove and the perpetually stewing teapot, I took advantage of the moment to slip out of the door. Relief and excitement turmoiled inside me as I hurried in the twilight across Aunt Ginny's 'fowd' past our kitchen window, and to the entry at the side of the house.

In this entry, my cousins and I put on plays and sang and 'tap danced' through all the popular songs we heard on the wireless. We played two ball for hours against the side of the house, vying with each other to see how high we could bounce the balls. On bonfire night, we ran up and down the entry, clutching each other and screaming in terror when the big boys from next door threw bangers and jumping jacks at us from behind their shields of dustbin lids.

Now, as I stood at the top of the entry, my whole attention was focused on the figure that came through the opening in the square bricked council built wall. My mother was slim and graceful, with that lingering element of film star beauty that had been all the rage in the 1940's, a decade ago.

Her eyes were green, her hair, dark and wavy, hidden beneath the intricate folds of the turban which, along with the cross over cotton pinafore beneath her coat, marked her out as a worker.

As she came towards me, half hidden in the shadows of the dying afternoon, it was as if the moment became suspended. My own bubble of fear and insecurity suddenly burst into the knowledge, too deep for works, that now she was here, everything would be all right. My brother and I were safe.

On her part, I sensed a surge of gratification and new energy as, with an almost clumsy gesture, she pressed me to her side. Whatever demands and difficulties had made up her long day, work was over now, not only for the night, but right up until Monday morning.

Within a couple of hours, she'd be happily opening the lid of her new gramaphone and putting on the one record that made up her collection. 'Wilomenah is plump and round!' she'd sing almost mischievously as she caught up with the dusting, and we'd need no encouragement at all to join in as we danced around the kitchen.

'Where's our Dave?' she asked, and, looking up, I saw her face, all alight with smiling. I breathed in deeply, catching the sharp, unmistakable smell of factory slurry oil and with it, mingling strangely and yet so sweetly, the rare sharpness of fresh fruit. 'I've brought yer some strawberries fer yer tay!'

TWO

'Theer 'e is, look! Wave to yer dad!'

Obediently, I squinted up at the far away upstairs window, and waved my hand. Dudley Guest hospital seemed very big, and it felt strange not to be allowed to go inside.

Still, Nan had encouraged us on the bus, we COULD stand on the wall while she and Mom took it in turns to go in, and if we were really lucky, Dad would be able to see us. And wave.

'Where?' Dave's frustrated voice rose as he wobbled on tiptoe beside me. The wall was slippery, topped with iron railings and prickly bushes ran along its vast, impenetrable length, pushing into our legs. 'I cor see him!'

'Can't.' Nan corrected, automatically, and then, as a faint movement came at the window. 'Theer, look! That's 'is arm - waving to yer both!'

I screwed up my eyes even further, trying to recognise the dismembered arm. But it had been so long now since Dad's accident that I sometimes wondered if I would recognise any of him, let alone a single arm.

'It'll be a long job,' Nan told everyone who asked about him, and lots who didn't. 'E's bin fower months in the Guest, and soon, it's off to Patsull 'all for 'is convalescence..!.'

The hand stopped waving, withdrawn as suddenly as it had appeared in the window frame, and Nan sighed. 'Come on,' she said, lifting us both from the wall. 'Visiting's over now. Yer Mom'll be out soon.'

On the way home on the bus, she suddenly opened her black handbag and took out a paper twist of sweets, chocolate drops encrusted with hundreds and thousands, crunchy and damply delicious against the tongue.

'Thanks, Nanna,' I said, leaning back against her comfortable bulk, while Mom lifted Dave onto her knee.

Nan looked over my head, taking in Mom's quiet, pale face, distracted by the visit and solemnly lovely. 'Dow thank me,' she said, meaningfully, 'Thank yer dad. 'E's the one who sent 'em for yer, out of the 'ospital - day 'e, Liza?'

As Mom nodded, surprise added sweetness to the unexpected treat in my mouth and relief lifted my spirits as I realised. Our dad must have forgiven us at last for causing him to crash his motor bike! The chocolate drops were a tangible sign of that - new sweets in return for the ones I never saw, that had been found in his jacket pocket on that day when everything had changed.

From then on, it seemed natural to link his hospital life with my own routine through the common denominator of food. `Me dad `as this in the hospital,` I`d say, as I unrolled and began to eat, lengthways, a slice of jammy swiss roll, only to be told sharply that my dad didn`t eat it like THAT!

The day came for Dad to go to Patsull, an ancestral hall which had been turned into a convalescent home. Though only about ten miles away, on the other side of Wolverhampton, it might as well have been on the other side of the world.

As usual, all the information came through Nan, who told whoever was lisening that `our `Arold` would be taken, along with his crutches, in the ambulance, early on the Saturday morning.

In the middle of Friday night, I was woken up by a sudden commotion from downstairs.

Creeping, shivering, onto the lino covered landing, I peered through the bannisters at the scene below. Granny Coley and Aunt Maud were both snoring loudly in the bedroom next door, and I had left my brother, also sleeping soundly, in the feather bed we shared .

`Oo is it?` Mom`s astonished figure nervously opened the front door to the tall, awkwardly determined man on crutches. The blast of cold darkness from outside filled with Mom`s remonstrations and Dad`s sketchy but bold description of his escape from Dudley Guest as he fell into her arms.

Mom sighed and shook her head as he told of stealing a coat from a lobby cupboard and sneaking out in it after Sister had done her late night ward round. By the time he got to the part about hobbling through the dark streets and along the cut towpath, his voice carrying through the house, my brother and I were both at his knee, listening, wide eyed with wonder and admiration.

`Well it`s too lert ter goo back now,` Mom said, as we  bore our hero towards the kitchen. `Berra mek some cocoa, `

Next morning, there came a fierce banging at the front door, and unknown disapproving male voices in the hall. Dave and I had just been getting used to having Dad around again, a muscular figure whose crutches seemed to fill the small living room, and who had so many interesting stories to tell. Now, the men in the ambulance had come to take him away again.

`You might think you`ve got away with it, my lad,` said the older man, as he stood by the open door. `but if anything comes of this escapade the doctors would be within their rights not to treat you!`

9

Whatever that meant, it was obvious to me. As he winked his eye, picked up his crutches, and prepared to go to Patsull, our Dad was just glad to have been home to see us all!

THREE

It was while dad was away at Patsull that Mrs. Miller put her head in the gas oven. The whisper went round the streets and finally caught up with us kids, playing in the disused anderson shelter at the bottom of our garden.

'Why did 'er do that?' I asked my cousin, Eva and was told with a knowing look it was because Mrs Miller was having another babby.

'This one'll mek thirteen,' Eva said, casually pulling a peach she had stolen from Jimmy Tarr's fruit shop from the leg of her navy blue knickers. 'Want a bite o' this?'

I hastily shook my head, digging my toe in the dirt floor of the tin shelter as I thought about Mrs. Miller's dilemna. How must it have felt, to put your head in the gas oven and wait to die? I couldn't imagine it, and it was too deep and scarey to try for long.

In the house, Mom was talking about it as she poured Granny Coley's tea. 'Gud job Mrs. Grainger come to the back door an' smelt the gas, Gran,' she said, as the old lady nodded from her place by the fire. ''er threatened it this time last year, if yo remember, when her got catched wi' young Pearl.'

'Ar, the poor wench'll 'ave one on every quarry tile afore E'S finished with 'er!' Granny Coley prophesied as she pulled her shawl more closely round her ninety year old shoulders, and meaningfully sniffed. We all thought silently about Mr Miller - a weasley looking man who went past to the pub every Friday night.

Suddenly noticing me in the doorway, she pushed out a boney hand. 'C'mere, cock. Let's see if I've gorra copper fer yer!'

Mom tutted her disapproval, but Granny ignored her. Opening her worn, flap over purse, she found a coin for myself and my brother. 'Ere, 'ave this penny apiece. Goo and get some suck!'

Clutching the big, brown pennies, we hurried up the road to the sweet shop kept by Jimmy Tarr's brother, Sid. There, it was possible to buy two 'hard juice' liquorice sticks, a paper full of 'kali' powder, or an everlasting strip for a penny.

'I'll 'ave an everlasting strip,' I told Dave decisively.'They last forever!' As we later walked home, I sucked thoughtfully at the thin toffee bar, filled as usual with the hope the magical name always gave me.

The sweet was just breaking, as usual, into disappearing bits as we turned back into West Road. The Miller family lived on the corner, separated from our house by broken palings and a patch of dirt. Hanging around the side of the house were children of all ages and both sexes while others played in the uncultivated back garden.

The youngest but two, a white haired toddler called Sheila sat on the ground eating dirt off a broken teaspoon. She was wearing a torn and filthy pink cotton dress and her legs and feet were bare.

Thinking of her mother and the gas oven, I stopped and broke off a big piece of the everlasting strip, now looking decidedly worse for wear. `Ere yow am, Sheila ` I said, holding it by the palings.

Like a shot, Sheila dropped the spoon and came towards me, her mouth and hands streaked with the blackness of the earth. She didn`t say thank you, but just the look on her face made the sacrifice complete.

When we got back into the house, it was obvious that Mom and Granny Coley had had `words.` `Words` were what I often overheard from Granny and Aunt Maud`s bedroom, when, late at night the two old ladies sat up in their feather bed and hissed and disagreed with each other about the treatment they were receiving at the hands of my mother.

`Er as we pension, yow` know, Our Mother! Ever`y penny goos into `er puss, when `er`s bin to the post office!`

`Dow be ser saft, Maud! Er`s runnin` the `wum, ay `er? An` now `Arold`s away, laid up in the `ospital, `er`s got `er work cut out!`

Now, the `words` had been serious enough to set Granny Coley`s mouth in a thin, tight line, while Mom`s face was white, and her green eyes bright with unshed tears. In her hands, she held the copy of `Wilomenah` in its brown paper sleeve.

` Ar, the gramaphone`s gone!` she intercepted as Dave and I both stared in amazement at the empty patch of lino on which had stood her pride and joy. `They`ve bin an` fetched it back cos I got behind with the payments!`

`PAYMINTS !` Granny Coley muttered. `Shouldn`t `ave `ad it if yow couldn`t afford it! - Never bin so ashamed as when that van come to the door - an` all the neighbours gawpin` -knowin` we business!`

That evening, to make matters worse, the last penny ran out in the electric light meter. As we were plunged into darkness, Mom jumped to her feet and hurried into the brick coal hole, which led directly off the kitchen.

`We`ll build up the fire wi` slack an` find out all the candles,` she said. `Now stop schraaching, yow two - and dow worry, Gran. We`ll soon `ave some light again.`

Before long, she had banked up the fire and filled the kettle at the kitchen sink, ready for the long business of making tea which I knew would taste all smokey from the black leaded grate. Deftly lighting candle stubs, she let a drop of wax fall into the saucers and tin lids which were our candlesticks.

The small room was filled with a strange and silent glow and I watched, as if suspended, the shadow of Granny Coley, hunched and immobile in her armchair, growing vast and travelling up the wall and across the ceiling. As usual, my brother started to try to make the shadows of birds and animals with his fingers, while from the table the usually silent Aunt Maud began to describe how, in the days before electricity, she used to make the white cotton covers for gas mantles.

`I crotcheted 'em, see,` she pushed gnarled hands into the shadowy room. `When I got back from the glass works, y'know!`

`Yes, Aunt Maud.`I nodded, remembering what I'd overheard about the old lady's habits of forgetfulness. My mother was always complaining that she took food, usually fruit she had bought from Jimmy Tarr's, and hid it in the bedroom, meaning to eat it but always forgetting, so that its rich, rancid smell would eventually fill the house.

But we loved her stories about the canalside glassworks where she had worked for forty years, especially the vivid descriptions of the glass blowers making the lampshades that were designed to hang from chains in people's living rooms.

`They use a big, long pipe -wi' a little blob o' glass on the end,` Aunt Maud said now, her thin face beneath the cap of white hair growing animated in the candlelight. `Real bobby dazzlers they mek, all outa that little blob! An' at the finish, they all come to me to be washed all clean an' bright in me big sink afore they got packed!`

How many lampshades would Aunt Maud have washed in forty years, I wondered idly before realising it sounded like a sum we might be given at school. Glancing at my mother's tired face, I realised she would soon be packing my brother and I off to bed, cocoa-less and without the comforting accompanyment of either radio or radiogram from downstairs.

`Tell we another story, Aunt Maud,` I begged, as the broken candles began to go out and the fire spluttered under the weight of the blackened kettle. `Tell we about when you went 'op-pickin'!` Scooting across the floor on my bottom, I settled against her legs, reluctant to ever be moved.

FOUR

'Hands on heads!' At the signal from Mrs Whitecraft, we all sat to attention in the narrow desks at St Mark's C. of E Junior school, Spring Street. From my seat at the dunces end of the class, I saw the headmaster, Mr Lodge, coming along the corridor with two other figures I vaguely recognised from West Road.

As they entered the classroom, propelled by a push from Mr Lodge, I saw to my horror that their heads were shaved and covered in sores which had been painted in purple gentian, the tell tale signs of the infectious skin complaint, impetigo.

'I want you all to take a look at these two individuals and learn a lesson from them, best beloved!' the headmaster boomed, as the boys shuffled their feet and stared fixedly at the floor. 'Mrs Whitecraft and I both know where they come from!' He exchanged a meaningful nod with the stiff backed teacher. 'And we both know where they will end up - as road sweepers, or worse, in prison! Shun them and their impertigo, best beloved, and make sure you never become dirty and low like them!'

As the boys were taken to be exhibited to the class beyond the school's sliding partition, I wondered why their mother had sent them to school with the impetigo. When Dave and I had picked it up from a playmate last year, we were kept away - wearing hats and walking to the park, scurrying with our mother past the noise of the school playground. Impetigo had been a scourge, like nits, and certainly not something to be put on display.

'Hands off heads! Time for tables!' As Mrs Whitecraft gave the usual command, I held my breath, half heartedly joining in the chorus of the hated multiplication tables, and hoping against hope I wouldn't be called upon to do a sum on my own.

My thoughts were still on Mr Lodge's visit and his scathing words about where the shaven headed boys came from. North, South, East and West roads were all part of the 'Lost City' slum clearance area of council houses.

It was a place cut off by canal banks and further isolated by the local electricity station, with its dank and ugly cooling towers. Inhabited by rag and bone men whose horses and carts were interspersed with the odd abandoned car, its few streets seemed to hold most of the largest and all of the toughest families in Tipton.

I knew without even looking round me that all the kids who sat at the dunces end of Mrs Whitecraft's class came, like me, from the Lost City. And it

'I want you to take a look at these two individuals . . . .'

15

was then, remembering what Mr Lodge had said about road sweepers and prisons, that I decided that I wasn't going to stay on the dunce's side any longer!

At the exact opposite of the class, the two seats nearest the window were always occupied by Mary Gregory and her friend, Pamela Simms. These two godlike creatures were, to my eyes, on a plain apart. Not only did they answer all the questions Mrs Whitecraft could throw their way, they were smartly dressed, had parents who took them to church, and possessed all the pens, books and pencil crayons they could possibly need for school work.

It was a forgone conclusion, that every week when we had our 'class test', it would be Mary and Pamela who would get most marks and vie for top place. Until now!

As I bent over the paper that Thursday afternoon, I felt my breath quicken. Suddenly, I just knew I could do this. It was as if I'd just woken up from a long sleep, especially when I saw this week's test was all about writing a story based on a book we had recently read.

My book collection, like my mother's record collection, comprised only one. I had read and re-read 'Little Women' endless times since Nan gave it to me for my birthday, and soon, I lost myself in the world of Meg, Jo, Beth and Amy.

Next day, when Mrs. Whitecraft came into the class room, she seemed somewhat subdued. Unlike most weeks, she did not hurry with the test results, beaming on her star pupils as she handed out their accolades. Instead, she shuffled the papers and sat at her big desk, looking uncertain and embarrassed.

Finally, she got up and began to give the papers back, starting as usual with the dunce's side, building up the excitement for the successful ones who deserved to savour it. My mouth went dry as I realised mine wasn't coming back, and moreover, that Mrs Whitcroft was avoiding looking in my direction at all!

With a sigh, she walked to the top of the class and wordlessly handed Mary and Pamela their papers. I saw them exchange a surprised look as she went back and sat down again, one paper still in her hand. But held near the corner, almost as if she was afraid she would catch something from it.

'Er, this week there has been quite a surprise,' she began, clearing her throat, and still not looking at me. 'The highest mark in the test has been achieved by Carol Sheldon. Well done, Carol.'

In the stunned silence that followed, I felt my heart leap in both delight and terror. Delight because I had done it, terror at the magnitude of what I had actually done. How was I going to get on, sitting with Mary Gregory and Carol Simms, with their spotless dresses and acceptable ways? I didn't even have a pencil case to take to the top desk, so bathed in sunlight from the great sash window. How could I do the school work without the equipment I knew my family couldn`t afford to provide?

Mrs Whitecraft cleared her throat, her stern face darkening with colour as, trembling with anticipation and pride, I began to get to my feet. Quickly, she held out a restraining hand more forbidding than any five barred gate.

`It`s all right, Carol,` she said, quickly, `You can stay where you are. This week`s test was just a practice.`

FIVE

Dad was home at last, brought back from Patsull late one Friday afternoon in the same ambulance that had taken him away. The ambulance was immediately mobbed with excited and curious children so that I had trouble getting near the figure in crutches that emerged.

'Dad! Dad!' I finally pushed through to his side, and he reached down to awkwardly ruffle my hair.

'Yow've sprung up,' he commented, and then, setting his face forward, he began to make his way on the crutches through the gate and up to the front door, where Mom was waiting, Dave fidgeting excitedly at her side.

'Lift me up! I cor see!'

Once in the house, Dad was given the place of honour on the couch in the scarcely used front room, where a fire had been lit to welcome him. The furniture gleamed, the space where the gramophone had been filled by Granny Coley's big old fashioned sideboard.

While Aunt Maud went to put the kettle on, Mom took her place almost shyly at Dad's side while Dave and I sat on the floor.

'Well, this is a bit different to Patsull 'all,' Dad grinned, as he eased his leg along the horsehair couch. He began to describe the convalescent hospital, and within seconds, I could see the upstairs wards with the smart and busy nurses, and the long, sweeping staircase, in my mind's eye.

'Guess wot, our Carol? We 'ad a visit from Queen Mary last wick!' he went on, obviously enjoying the way my mouth dropped open in awe. 'All the poor buggers in the upstairs wards struggled along the landing and down the stairs, nearly breakin' their necks to get outside to see 'er! Some of em couldn't 'obble more than a few steps. In the end, there was on'y me still left in bed!'

'Day YOW want to see Queen Mary then, our 'arold?' I realised that while he'd been speaking, Nan had arrived, her shopping bag full of goodies for the invalid.

Grinning, Dad reached out for a grape and polished it on his sleeve before popping it into my brother's mouth. 'That's what the matron asked me,' he replied, ' but I tode 'er straight. If Queen Mary wants to see me - let 'er come up 'ere!'

The next afternoon, in the Anderson shelter, I recounted the story to Big Aunt Ginny's children. Though I didn't really understand it, I sensed it made my dad a hero, of sorts, someone who made up his own mind about things.

Now he was back, everything would be all right, I told myself. Mom would be able to stay at home again, and there would be no more need for Dave and I to go to Aunt Ginny's.

On Monday afternoon, I walked home with Eva and her sister Rose as always, collecting Dave from the infants on the way. Mrs. Whitecraft had been unusually encouraging, giving me nine out of ten for my English composition.

But I no longer aspired to sit at the top of the class. My dreams had taken a different turn, and it was all thanks to Carroll Levis, and his radio 'Discoveries.'

'Did yow 'ear 'im on the wireless yesterday?' I asked my companions enthusiastically. Just the memory of the entertainers warm, drawling voice - the knowledge that we shared the same Christian name - was enough to make me want to dance through the whole 'Lost City'.

'This wench was on - 'on'y six, an' 'er sung, just like we do in the entry!'

In my fruitful imagination, the girl had been wearing a red satin skirt, just like the one Nan had promised to make me one day. A skirt which whirled and sparkled, as it danced along with you.

'If I give my heart to yoooooo!' I warbled, off key, as we at last reached the entry which was our theatre. 'Will you promise to be trooooo! Now my dad's 'um, I'm goin' to ask 'im to write to Carrol Levis and get me on the wireless! After all, 'e nearly met Queen Mary!'

SIX

'They've set somebody else on while I've bin in the 'ospital!' All my dreams of fame and fortune crashed around me as I overheard my parents conversation.

Dad had come in late for his tea and I could tell from the smell on his breath that he'd called in at the 'Golden Cup'

Washed out from her day at the factory, Mom snapped back at him;' Yow said they'd keep your job open! What'll we do now?'

She looked around her as if trapped, and for some reason I suddenly remembered the stories she'd told me about her own mother dying when she was just a baby and her father running off with somebody else. She was an orphan, and the thought of that always made me sad and shivery.

'Well, it ay my fault they've done the dirty on me!' Dad's blue eyes flashed and he snatched up the coat he had just taken off. He too looked around, at the two old ladies whose disapproving silence filled the poky living room, my brother, just starting to grizzle for his tea, me, horrified, swallowing every word and gesture whole.

'Ar'm off out!' he announced, and a moment later, the back door slammed.

'Good riddance!' Mom spat the words between gritted teeth before launching into a turmoil of frenzied activity. Within minutes, the fire was made up and a meal of baked beans, fried eggs and bacon set out on the table.

Chairs were silently pulled out and cups of tea made and poured from the brown earthenware pot.

'Dow worry, my wench,' Granny Coley said, as she came across from the fireside with her stick in hand.

'Ar, Liza,. E'll be back.' Aunt Maud put in knowingly, 'An' e'll soon get another job, p'raps even at the glassworks!'

Mom, busy cutting bread from the thick white loaf, merely nodded. Her green eyes were both sad and angry, and I sighed as I climbed onto my chair. Even though it wasn't Friday, our traditional bath night, I had a feeling my brother and I would be scrubbed from head to toe in the tin bath on the hearth tonight. Packed off to bed while it was still light, I knew I'd lie there long after Dave was asleep, my head still tingling from the onslaught with the steel nit comb, my stomach rumbling because of the obligatory dose of Syrup of Figs.

Aunt Maud's prophetic words came true a few days later. Dad did get a new job. But it wasn't at the canalside glassworks. It was at the Austin car factory, far away in Birmingham!

'It's awl right for some! E'll be on twenty quid a wick now!' I heard Aunt Ginny say to one of the neighbours, as she pegged out her washing in the back yard. 'I s'pose it'll be all swank, then, with no thoughts of them that's looked after the bloody kids fer nothin!'

As she nodded in our direction, I took a deep breath. With no loose teeth in my head, and the prospect of freedom in view, I suddenly found the courage to blurt out:

'Why dow yow like we, Aunt Ginny? What've we done?'

Big Aunt Ginny's mouth dropped open, despatching the clothes pegs she'd been holding in it swiftly to the muddy path. Stepping back, she glared down at me from a great height, angry colour mounting her gaunt face.

'Oo'd yer think YO am, questionin' me, yer cheeky little bugger!' she burst out, spittle flying, as she seized and shook me. 'After all I've done for yer, and yo on'y a pack o - of bloody lodgers!'

She ranted on, finally dragging both Dave and myself away from the gawping neighbour and into the steamy back kitchen and the other children.

As Aunt Ginny turned to the wooden dolly tub and lifted the clothes pusher, I had two very different thoughts going through my head at the same time.

The first was, I was glad I wasn't one of those cotton shirts Aunt Ginny was bashing in the hot water and suds. The second was, I had to find out what 'lodgers' meant!

SEVEN

'We'm goin' to decorate!' Mom announced the Saturday after dad's first pay packet. She had a scarf on her head and her floral pinafore was fastened tightly around her middle. 'So yow two goo out to play!'

Dave had been interestedly stirring the bucket of 'whitewash' set carefully on the kitchen floor. 'Yeller, it's all yeller!' he exclaimed.

Nan, who had arrived to help, began to bundle us into our coats. 'It's ter do lemons,' she said, and as I frowned. 'Yow'll see, when it's finished. Now, gerrout from under we feet!'

I was only too glad to get out, hating the way the furniture had to be covered in old sheets, and the curtains taken down from the front room window. It made everything seem so unfamiliar.

Aunt Maud and Granny Coley were the lucky ones, I thought as I led my brother through the back door onto the yard. They'd been allowed to stay in bed until all the disruption was over!

When I looked into the Anderson shelter, Eva was sitting on her coat, industriously corking, thin, nail bitten fingers flying as she passed the blue wool between the nails, hammered into an old cotton reel.

'Shut the door, quick!' she hissed. 'I'm 'iding from our mother, mekking a pair of slippers!'

Only too glad of the invitation, I shoved Dave in the general direction of a group of marble playing lads and went inside. Sitting down by Eva, the ridged sides of the shelter against my back, I watched her pull the short piece of knitting through the reel before asking the question:

'Ev. Yowr muther said we was on'y lodgers. What does it mean?'

Eva looked down on me from the height and experience of her twelve years. 'It means it ay yowr 'ouse!' she said, pointedly. 'It's Granny's name in the rent book not yer dad's - so er could mek yer leave any time 'er wanted!'

-Make us leave? I couldn't believe it, and I frowned at Eva uncomprehendingly. Vaguely, I understood that Granny Coley and Aunt Maud had lived together in an old house in Horseley Heath that had been pulled down before Mom and Dad got married. But 3 West Road was the only place I knew as home. I couldn't imagine being anywhere else.

22

Realising Eva was looking almost as triumphant as Big Aunt Ginny had, I jumped to my feet. 'It dow bother me!' I said with a confidence I certainly didn't feel. 'If I had ter leave, I'd goo an' live in a caravan like the gypos over the fields! That'd be really good!'

Later, hoping for a word with my mother, I sneaked back home through the open front door to find the house totally transformed! The front room walls, ceiling and paintwork were all covered with an uneven pattern of yellow blobs that even included the floor to ceiling cupboards.

'Like it?' beamed Mom, her face smudged beneath the loosened scarf. 'We dun it with sponges. It's all the rage, yer Nan says!'

'Ar, that's right, Lize, all the nobs've 'ad it dun!' Nan looked pinker and more exhilarated that I'd ever seen her. As the door creaked open and the two old ladies came suspiciously from upstairs, she called cheerily:

'That's it, Sarah. Come on in - yow an' all, Maud! Come and see what a difference a few lemons mek!'

'Thuz a lot of lemons!' My brother, tiring of marbles, appeared at my side, pointing in the direction of the living room.

'We 'ad some of the stuff left over.' The two painters looked at each other as the gasps of Granny and Maud carried back to them. 'So we thought we'd do in the scullery an' all!'

-'Wot the bloody 'ell's THIS!' The back door banged and Dad's raised, astonished voice was suddenly filling the place. He stormed in, eyes blazing, as he took in the continuing blobs which seemed to reach as far as the eye could see.

Like two guilty schoolgirls, the besmirched decorators stood in silence unable, it seemed, to look at him, no longer wanting to look at one another.

'It's lemons, 'Arold,' Nan said, unnecessarily. Suddenly, a wide smile broke across her face and a moment later, her shoulders started shaking with suppressed laughter.

'Ooo-er!' Irresistibly, Mom caught the giggle. As she looked again athe result of her day's labour, her hand was clasped across her mouth. 'D-dun yer think we've gorra bit carried away, cock?' she asked, rhetorically.

'Carried away?' Dad rolled up his sleeves and picked up the empty bucket. 'I should think the two on yer's 'ad spots in front of yer eyes!'

He marched into the kitchen and a moment later came back, with the bucket filled to the brim with water. 'Waesh 'em off!' he ordered as Mum and

Nan both stared at him aghast. `I mean it, Liza! Ar`m gooin` ter bed, and when I get up, I dow want to see even one lemon in either of these rooms!`

-`S`pose we`ll arrer do it!` There was no sign of Mom`s earlier enthusiasm as she sighed and went into the kitchen for some cleaning rags. `Come on, kids, yow c`n `elp me an` yer Nan waesh it off!`

While Granny Coley kept up a running commentary for the benefit of Aunt Maud, I stood by Nan, dipped a cloth in the cold water and experimentally wiped at one of the lower smudges. As it spread and ran and gradually disappeared, I thought it was a shame we couldn`t keep at least a few of the lemons. For a while, they had made everything look different.

EIGHT

'I'm askin' yer to LEAVE, Liza!' At first, I thought the urgently whispered words were part of my dream and I struggled to breathe in the dark, airless room. Then I realised the voice was coming, not from Granny Coley's room, but from where my parents slept, on the other side of the narrow landing. And it was Dad who was speaking!

Carefully not to wake my brother, I pushed off the heavy green eiderdown and lowered my bare feet to the cold lino. It seemed miles to the door, past the huge, oppressive dressing table, with its three mirrors, and the wardrobe which made it almost impossible to walk at the bottom of the bed.

The bedroom door was slightly ajar, and I prised it open further as I slipped through it. I stood, shivering in my thin pyjamas, as the icyness of the house seemed to descend damply over me.

Over the familiar sounds of Granny and Aunt Maud's night noises, I caught my mother's heartfelt sigh, followed by her whispered reply:

'Oh, 'Arold, I've told yer till I'm sick, I cor leave Gran. I promised I'd tek care on 'er fer as long as 'er needs me!'

Kneeling on the floor, I listened to dad's unhappy voice, trying to persaude her to move away from 3, West Road, and her agitated but still decisive reply:

'Gran took me in when I had nowheer ter goo. 'Er went out scrubbin' floors at the age of 70 because my own ferther was gonna 'ave me put in the workuss!' she reminded him. 'When the council gid 'er this 'ouse, 'er begged me not to leave her!'

-'Even though that means we'll never 'ave a plairce of we own? Yow, me and the kids?' Dad's reply was almost lost in the rumble of snores from the room next door, but I still caught the longing and the supressed anger of his tone.

Next day, when I got up for school, he had already gone to work, and Mom, pale faced but busier than ever, was sorting out the washing. 'I want yow ter goo to the butchers on yowr way 'um, Carol,' she said, picking up an old envelope and a stub of pencil. 'Gerra quarter o' sausage and two rashers o' Cumberland baercon fer yer dad's tay.'

'Aw -do I 'ave to?' After my disturbed night, the last thing I needed was a trek to the shop which, contrary to being 'on my way home' was actually nearly a mile in the opposite direction.

To my hurt surprise, Mom jabbed at me with the reddened hand she had been using to drop the clothes into the steaming dolly tub. Her green eyes flashed and I stepped instinctively backwards out of her reach.

`Ar, yow bloody well do!` she burst out, distractedly pushing a slice of bread and melted butter into my brother's hand. `I wo `ave time with all this waeshin` ter do! So gerroff ter school and do as yow`m tode!`

On the way home from the butchers, I stopped near the cooling towers and carefully undid the white wrapped parcel. Squeezing a small, pink lump of meat from one of the two sausages, I put it into my mouth and slowly savoured it as I made my suddenly reluctant way home.

I didn`t overhear any more talk about us leaving West Road. But over the next few months, Dad became a shadowy figure Dave and I scarcely ever saw. Busy with concerts in the entry, and struggles at school, I hardly missed him, though it was obvious from her white face and pinched lips that Mom did, very much.

Her unhappiness made her short tempered and we learnt to keep out of her way, especially when she was banging round in the coal shed, or furiously cleaning the windows with vinegar water and scrunched up newspaper.

Big Aunt Ginny no longer featured so largely in our lives, in fact, she acknowledged me with only a disapproving sniff, since my outburst in the back garden. As the seasons slipped by, and our street games went, unspokenly, from skipping ropes to hide and seek and back again, I began to long, like my father, for change and adventure in my life.

The only place it seemed to be available was in the pages of books, and in my imagination, I spent hours with Jo, Meg, Beth and Amy March, whose `Marmee`was at once too nice and wholly desirable. Unnoticed by Mrs Whitecraft, I read everthing I could take from the classroom book cupboard, from Peter Rabbit, to Pilgrims Progress.

Then Eva took me, early one Monday evening, to the public library in Toll End Road, an old, single storey building with wide steps leading up to revolving glass doors. And I fell through - like Alice - into another dimension.

`Come ON!` hissed Eva, wiping her hands on her cotton skirt as she led me up to the polished desk. `This is wheer we JOIN!`

Mesmerised, I was still staring round, trying to take in the wonderful, amazing sight and smell of so many books - thousands and thousands of them - on shelves all around the walls.

`Yes? What do you want?` The bespectacled librarian seemed very old and sterm, twice as formidable, if that were possible, as our school teachers. She peered from below her 'Silence' notice as if we were some lower form of life. Disgust and suspicion filled her narrow face as Eva, sniffing noisily, said we wanted to 'join.'

'You won't be able to take out any books today!' Although she didn't say it, I knew she had seen the tell tale 'Lost City' stamp on our foreheads, and was propelling us towards the dunces part of her library.

She explained about the important green card that had to be filled in and signed by somebody called a rate payer, and when all that had been done, we would have to pay a penny joining fee.

'Oh.' Eva's face fell at the enormity of it all. But as I took my green card and prepared to carry it carefully away, I was already working it out. Just how I could get that penny.

NINE

Dad was in the entry with Eileen Dawson when I got back from Nan's. I was a bit surprised because Eileen was `common`. She worked at the transport cafe, wore bright red lipstick and smoked cigarettes in the street. I'd heard the grown ups discussing what they called her `goings on` very often, though I never seemed quick enough to catch the precise, mysterious details.

`So long, then,` Dad straightened up from where he seemed to have been standing quite close to Eileen. She patted her hair and smiled before teetering away on high heels.

`Ta ra then, `Al,` she called over her shoulder, her voice sounding low and almost challenging. I frowned, not only at her tone, but at the shortening of his name, but he didn't seem to notice its strangeness.

`An what yow bin up to, our Carol?` he asked, leading me companionably towards the back door. I needed no second bidding to describe how Nan had agreed to sign my green card, and, more to the point, give me the penny I needed to join the library. A warm glow seemed to spread inside me as I remembered how Nan had listened, sitting side by side with me on the sofa.

`I dow own me own `ouse, so I dow know if I AM a ratepayer!` she'd admitted finally, biting her lip as she read through the card again. `P`raps I'll get into trouble for signin` this?`

Then, she'd looked at my crestfallen face, and hers had softened. `Giz it `ere. Yow`m wuth any trouble, an` I'll gi` yer the penny wi` pleasure!`

The next night, I sat by the fire reading my first library book, while Mom made a rag rug for the hearth. I knew it was for Christmas which would, so Nan said, be better than we'd hoped this year, now Dad had his job at the Austin.

The rug was to be a mixture of black, red and green, all strips cut up from clothes too old to be even given to the rag and bone man. Mom had bought a sack and cut it open and washed it before taking her `podger` - a sharpened clothes peg - and pushing the strips of cloth through.

`I'd goo mad if I day ave this ter do,` she said suddenly, simply, addressing me as if I were an adult. I nodded, knowing her despair had something to do with the way Dad had got changed into his best shirt and gone out, as she was helping Granny and Aunt Maud to bed.

Long after the lights were out, I lay in bed waiting for the sounds of my father coming home, but I must have fallen asleep because I never heard him return to the house, and he'd gone off to catch the works coach to Birmingham before we got up for school.

Two days later, on Saturday, Aunt Maud took us to buy our Christmas presents. Every year, a little procession, comprising Dave and myself and Aunt Ginny's three youngest accompanied her to the toy shop near the glassworks at Dudley Port.

As we walked, Aunt Maud's white head bobbed. 'I used to work at them glass works, yer know...'

I smiled as I fell into step with Eva and Rose, anticipating the shop, stacked from floor to ceiling with toys. The more expensive ones, the baby dolls with closing eyes and plastic shoes, and the bright realistic train sets with their metal tracks, were well out of our range. But Aunt Maud, despite her absentmindedness, never forgot what she COULD afford.

'Toy suck shaps, skippin' ropes.' As she entered the shop like a ship in full sail with the crowd of us in her billowing sails, she glanced from Rose to her brother Joey and at his side, a saucer eyed Dave. 'An let's see some dinky cars an tool kits fer these lads!'

The shop keeper was tall and thin and wore a brown overall. I could tell the way he gulped and glanced at his watch that he remembered us from last year. 'Yes, missis,' With one eye on Aunt Maud's closely clutched purse, and the other on Eva, who had wandered away to where an array of plastic dolls were stacked, he struggled to stay in control. 'Toy sweet shops? We've had some new ones in for this Christmas with their own weighin' scales.'

He put the box on the glass fronted counter, and I caught a glimpse of the miniature sweet jars, the tiny paper bags, and cardboard money and the pink scales, all displayed against a brightly coloured 'sweet shop' background.'

'C'n I 'ave one, Auntie Maud?' Rose asked eagerly, tugging at our great aunt's voluminous skirt. I knew she was anticipating the joys of selling the tiny dolly mixtures and fruit jellies, and could almost taste them on my own tongue.

'That's one settled, then!' Aunt Maud's false teeth flashed a smile at the visibly relieved shopkeeper. 'Now wot about yow other wenches - dun yer want the serm?'

Eva and I looked at each other, both certain of what we didn't want. 'A knittin' set, please,' Eva said, pointing to a busy looking box just behind the shop keeper's head.

While it was reached down, and placed on the counter with Rose's sweetshop, I felt everyone's eyes on me.

'Urry up, our Carol,` my brother urged, eager to choose his dinky car. With six year old wisdom, he looked up at his mate, our cousin, Joey 'Bet er dow know what her wants,` he wagered.

That was where he was quite wrong. Ever since we'd come into the Alladin's cave of the shop, there had been only one treasure I'd had my heart set on.

'A writin` set,` I burst out eagerly, pointing to the cream and gold box in the very corner of the counter display. 'Wi` paerper an` env'lopes, an` all them little stamps!`

TEN

'Dow cry, Dave!' Torn between embarrassment and sympathy, I handed my sobbing brother the bit of torn sheeting that served as my hankie. All the other kids who were spilling out of Ocker Hill infants to be met by their mothers seemed to be staring. And listening as my brother noisily broke his heart about not having a school Christmas party.

'Yow'm too big, now - that's just for the babbies' class!' I tried to make it sound encouraging. But I couldn't help feeling cheated on his behalf as I realised just how much he had been looking forward to a repeat of last year's end of term party.

'We'll have we own party on Saturday,' I promised, hurrying him away from the prying eyes of our cousins and the ever present group of curious Miller children who followed raggedly after them. 'A proper feast wi' oranges an pop from Nan's, an - an' fruit gums!'

Dave gave me back my hankie and wiped his nose on his sleeve. 'C'n I ave the black uns?' he asked, craftily. 'All the black uns?'

I looked back at the new infants with their clutched parcels and jelly streaked faces. 'Oh, aw right,' I acquiesced, knowing even then I'd live to regret my generosity.

At home, we found to our surprise that Dad was home early, the car factory having finished for the Christmas break. Mom was busy frying bacon for our tea, and there was a great big smile on her face.

'Goo 'n' see wot yer dad's brought me fer Christmas!' she greeted. 'It's in the front room, in the bay winder!'

Curiously, we hurried into the 'best' room, to find Granny Coley huddled in her shawl by the unlit fire. 'Dog!' she sniffed, nodding her head. 'Theer - look - waerstin' good money on trankelments!'

I glanced warily back towards the living room while Dave dashed to the window ledge. 'Cor, look at this!' he breathed, all his earlier upset forgotten.

I stood by his side, breathing deeply as I stared at the big statue, an Alsatian dog made out of chalk, with realistic markings and a red, open mouth, complete with painted teeth. The front paws were crossed, and the long tail curled round on the imitation grass base.

'It's BEAUTIFUL!' I sighed, ignoring Granny's second sniff. As I ran back in the direction of the tantalising bacon smell, I understood perfectly why Mom loved the dog so much. Not only did it add style to the room she spend

31

so much time keeping spotless, but it was a present from Dad. Showing her, and everyone else, how much he loved her!

Christmas, I felt sure, <u>was</u> going to be better than ever this year, and it started next day, Christmas Eve, when all four of us walked to Great Bridge to do the shopping.

The cold air seemed to crackle with expectancy around the market and the shops, and people called out greetings to each other as they hurried busily along.

`Fust we get the bird, then the Christmas tree,` Mum seemed to have the special shopping list in her head and for once, Dad was happy to take part, moving the feathered chicken from one arm to the other as he prepared to lift the small, spindly tree over his shoulder.

Nuts, tangerines, dates and figs were all bought at Adams' huge fruit and vegetable shop, along with the potatoes, carrots and brussel sprouts which would help fill our plates on Christmas day.

We were just waiting for Mom to come out of Firkin's cake shop with the Christmas pudding when a voice called. `Arold! I thought it was yow!`

The familiar figure of Nan hurried over to us. `Good job it`s on`y once a year!` she said, typically. `I`ve left yer grandad pluckin` the turkey!`

Before disappearing in the direction of the market, she reminded Dave and myself .`I`ll see yow kids in the mornin` Arn gorra surprise fer both of yer !`

`A red satin skirt! That`s what MY surprise` ll be!` I grandly told my cousins that afternoon when, banished by the busy grown ups, we crowded into the damp and chilly shelter. `My Nan said `er`d mek me one aerges agoo!`

Eva glanced at me and I caught the unmistakable gleam of envy in her eyes before she stuck her thin nose into the cold air and said: `Well, WE`M `avin` sucklin` pig fer dinner - me Dad`s gone to the country to fetch it! An` our muther says a full bally c`n allus loff at fine clooz!`

A full belly AND fine clothes. Next day,. I experienced the good fortune of having both. It didn`t matter that dad, after taking us to our grandparents, went off to the pub and made us late getting home for dinner. The dinner was waiting, with Granny and Aunt Maud at the table, proudly wearing under their long skirts, the knitted garters I`d made them for Christmas.

There was home made ginger beer to wash down a chicken that had been cooked to perfection. And Mom smiled, her face shining with happiness, as she carefully poured a thimbleful of medicinal brandy onto the pudding and carried, wreathed in blue flames, to the table. `Ready! Deep breath - now - all mek a wish!`

The satin skirt was a full circle of breathtaking scarlet. While my brother played with his surprise - an old wind up gramophone with Woolworths cowboys and indians glued round the rim, I whirled and stamped. And dreamt to my heart's delight.

ELEVEN

Going to fetch the coal was the worst errand in the world, and I was really glad I didn't have to do it on my own. Between them, Aunt Ginny and Mom had worked out a system whereby they shared the cost of a pram load and also got free child labour for the day.

'It's <u>miles</u> away!' I complained as my cousins waited in the entry with the huge battered pram with its high wheels and broken hood. 'An' it's all up - hill!'

'Dow be so saft, Carol. The wharf's on'y in New Road!' Since Christmas, Mom had seemed busier, and sharper than ever, her face growing more grim each time Dad got all dressed up to go out.

Now, she scrubbed at the draining board, energetically sending sprays of Sunlight soap up into the cold January air. 'Anyroad, yer con get yer coot on and goo wi' Eva an' them,' she said, giving me a push towards the door. 'We'm right on rock bottom in that coal 'ole!'

'Ar, an we'n run out of ode shoes to burn an all, my wench!' Granny Coley called from the chair where she sat, wrapped up in an old army greatcoat. 'It'll feel like corn in Egypt when yo gets back with some nutty slack!'

Only slightly placated, I put on my tweed coat and the pixie hat and scarf Nan had knitted that touched the ground. 'C'mere.' Eva deftly tied the ends around my back, strait jacket style. 'Yow get that side with our Terry,' she ordered as we began to push the unwieldy pram out towards the icy streets.

I had only been partly right about the way to the coal wharf being up hill. At the top of the 'Mot' bridge there was a steep incline and the pram took off at speed, so that I more than once lost my footing and skidded under its careering wheels, banging my chin on the hard, wobbling handle.

'See that trolley?' panted 11 year old Terry, nudging me in the side. Turning my head, I saw a homemade box on wheels, being pulled to the top of the hill by a lad I vaguely recognised from school. 'Soon as our mother's dun wi' this pram, I'm mekkin' a trolley like that!' Terry bragged. 'Yowr Dave c'n come on it, if 'e waents!'

I nodded, trying to feel pleased for my brother. I knew better than to ask if there would be room on the trolley for me. Some things, like fire cans and fishing in the cut, were exclusively for boys.

As we made our slow way home with the laden pram rocking from side to side, I passed the time day dreaming. Kathy Froggatt, who lived next

'I'm mekkin' a trolley like that!' Terry bragged.

door to the Millers, had come round to our house the night before talking about a special party in the street.

'We'm doin' it fer the Corrynation, see, cock,' she told Mom, 'Collectin' so's all the little uns can 'ave a gud time on June 3rd!'

'So long as there's no 'ire purchise,' Granny Coley still hadn't forgotten the shame of the returned gramaphone. 'We likes to pay we own road in this 'ouse!' she called out sharply.

As Mom sighed and quickly moved onto the doorstep, Mrs. Frogatt explained that a weekly collection would be made, sixpence for each child to provide for party food and drink, and a coronation mug to take home.

It all sounded so exciting. Not only were we getting a new Queen - Elizabeth the Second - but even the kids from the Lost City were to be included in the celebrations. All I hoped was that running out of coal didn't also mean we'd run out of money, because then Mom wouldn't be able to keep up the weekly payments!

TWELVE

'We've just sid the QUEEN on a little box at me Nan's house!' I was so excited I didn't think twice about blurting out the news into my great aunt's crowded kitchen. Several heads, including Big Aunt Ginny's, swivelled round to stare at me.

'Awright for some!' Ginny sniffed, and then, curiosity fighting with the disinterest in her face. 'Wor is this box then - a magic lantern thing?'

'No!' I frowned back, not quite knowing what a 'magic lantern' was. 'It's a television set! Yow c'n see pictures through it, an' Dave and me saw the Queen, plain as anythin'!'

It was, I thought privately, as I joined Rose on the rug, a million times better than the West Road Coronation party had turned out to be! Then, it had poured with rain, and all the children had been hastily snatched away from the tables and taken indoors by their parents.

'All YOW got was a dish o' trifle!' Mom couldn't get over it, and kept shaking her head. 'All them tanners, to say nothin' of the new rigouts!'

I was still wearing my 'rigout' - a red, white and blue cotton dress from the Friday night tally man's suitcase. I had thought it was beautiful and so original, until I saw Eva, Rose, and nearly every other small girl on the estate had an identical one!

Seeing the Queen on the television, though, was definitely something different! Forgetting that I could still be overhead by the rest of the family, I began to tell an open mouthed Rose all about the wonders I'd seen 'on the box.'

'An me dad says we'll be getting a television of we own as soon as he c'n serve up enough money!' I finished, excitedly.

'Huh! From what I'VE 'eard, e's fun other things to spend that on, these past few months!' Big Aunt Ginny muttered, as if to herself. And though she steadfastly avoided my questioning gaze, I knew she very definitely intended me to hear!

Next day, I used the excuse of taking my library book back to go again to Nan's.

'It's my little wench! Come on in, darlin'!' I was glad to see that Grandad was at work and Nan and I had the house to ourselves. She brewed tea and gave me a slice of her homemade fruit cake.

'Yow look as if yow need five minutes love!' Arms around each other, we rocked together on the sofa under the baleful glare of the small, television set which so transformed her tiny living room. 'Is someut' the marrer, cock?'

I shook my head, suddenly quite unable to find the words to express the uncertainty I was beginning to feel, deep inside. Nan looked more closely at me then nodded towards the magic box.

'See them potters 'ands!' We stared, fascinated at the lump of clay on the wooden board, being shaped and smoothed so gracefully before our very eyes on the screen 'I know they purrum on fer the 'Interlude. But .I could watch em all day!'

Leaning gratefully back against her apron, I drank in the peace being measured out by the gently ticking clock which had taught me to tell the time. In a minute, I knew Nan would be easily persuaded to lead me upstairs to show me her 'treasures', the lace edged pillowcases and the two plates with blue ribbon threaded through that had been a wedding present from her brother who was killed in the pit.

'Tell me about when yow was little, Nanna,.' I said. Though I knew them all off by heart, those stories were better than anything I found in my books. I could see the little back to back house in Netherton, with the noisy family of ten brothers and three sisters and Nan, the youngest, who was always described as the 'scraerpins up!'

In my mind's eye, I could imagine the cobbled yard, complete with privy and pig sty, and Nan's mother, Granny Smart, busily scrubbing the pig's back with a hard brush to make the cracklin' nicer.

As I later made my way over the steep Mot bridge, clutching the bag of toffees Nan had given me to take home and share with Dave, I felt I had been surrounded and fortified by love.

THIRTEEN

'A box o' dried peas, please, 'I asked Jimmy Tarr distractedly. As I handed over the handful of precious pennies my mother had given me, I thought about the strained atmosphere at home where, for some reason, Mom wasn't speaking to Dad again.

I hadn't dared complain about going on the errand, or even look, hopeful of a penny, in Granny Coley's direction. She too had lapsed into silence, coming out of it only to sigh deeply and shake her head at her inmost thoughts.

Only the day before, while Mom had been busy black leading the grate, I had sat and watched the mantlepiece clock for a whole five minutes, listening to its solemn ticking and amazing myself that Granny and I could both sit there and not speak for what seemed a very long time.

Taking the peas, I wandered out of the shop. The weather was warm. I knew lots of the bolder children would be swimming in the cut, enjoying the early evening sunshine. My Coronation frock felt heavy and itchy and the backs of my legs ached as I began to trail despondently back towards the streets of the Lost City.

On the corner of South Road, ahead of me, I saw a group of children, among them Janice Derby, whose proud boast was that she had 'lamped' every kid, male or female, in our street.

Janice was short, squat and brawny, with a permanent scowl, and she always seemed to be surrounded by younger brothers, sisters and cousins. Up until then, I'd studiously avoided her, going numb with terror every time it crossed my mind that I might one day unwittingly become her next victim.

Now, to make myself feel better, I began to rhythmically shake the box of dried peas. I nearer I got to Janice and her posse, the harder I shook, my body soon responding to the beat, my feet, skipping in order to keep up with it.

In a moment, I'd be safely past, round the corner and up the entry, giving the peas to my grim faced mother, who would be waiting, the water all ready for the overnight soak with the mysterious tablet of bicarbonate of soda.

'WHOOSH!' It was just as I drew level with Janice that it happened. The cardboard lid of the peas finally gave way and there was an enormous hard, greeen shower, falling all around me.

'SAFT bugger!' Janice's loud sneer rose over the screams of laughter of her mates. She came across the road, swaggering, pointing, as I stood gasping, trying desperately to snatch some of the fallen peas off my dress before they joined the rest in the gutter.

`YOW`LL get a lampin` now!` she crowed, putting all my cascading horror at the thought of going home into spite filled words. `Yer muther`ll kill yer!`

It was my mother's face, twisted with fury, that swam before me as I turned on Janice, all my fear of her gone in the desparate heat of the moment.

`Oh, shurrup, YOW!` I shouted. `Oo the bloody `ell d`yer think YOW am, anyway?`

I had one moment of glory as sheer astonishment made Janice gape at me almost like a frightened fish. Then, her expression changed and she looked me slowly up and down - twelve months younger and a lot smaller. With no experience of fighting except the occasional spat with my younger brother.

`I`ll get YOW, Carol Sheldon!` she threatened, one hard finger poking me in the chest. `YOW`ll be sorry yow swore at me!`

I couldn`t believe any of this was happening. But something told me not to cry, at least not until I was out of her sight. Clutching the empty pea box, I quickened my pace, needing to reach the safety of home yet reluctant to face what awaited me there.

`Hey Carol!`

`Wheer`s yer paes, Carol?`

`Wot yer throwed `em away for?`

I tried to pretend Janice and her cronies weren`t just a few yards behind me, catcalling and jeering. But when a stone, picked up from the gutter, caught me hard in the middle of the back, I couldn`t ignore their presence any longer.

`See yer termorra, Carol.` As I neared our gate, I saw a little group of women neighbours, gathered to talk in the pleasant evening sunlight. Janice`s mock friendly parting had been , I knew, for their benefit, not mine. Head down, I passed through the women who suddenly seemed to have gone quiet.

I still had to face my mother with the evidence of the empty pea box!

Next day, I woke up early and crept downstairs before Dad went out to catch the coach. His goodlooking face broke into a grin when he saw me: `Bin in a bit o` bother, aye `yer, our Carol?` he asked, knowingly.

I nodded resignedly and my heart thumped as I moved closer, thinking that in some miraculous, grown up way he knew about Janice and what she was threatening to do to me.

'I 'eard yow got sent ter bed early fer not doin` an errand right,` he said,and as I nodded again, trying to hide my disappointment, he reached out a hand to touch my cheek.

'Dow worry, cock,` he said, consolingly. 'Yer Mom allus manages to find summat fer we tay - an` ter tell yer the truth, I cor stond dried paes meself!`

FOURTEEN

'Dear Carrol Levis,' I wrote painstakingly on the cream coloured writing paper I'd had for Christmas. 'I should like to be one of your Discoveries.....'

Though I didn't know the celebrity's address, and in any case had no money for postage, just writing the letter gave me comfort. When it was finished, I folded it carefully into an envelope and hid it in the shoe box under the bed where I kept my copy of 'Little Women' and a red notebook Nan had given me.

In the notebook, I had written a story about a sad wireless set which didn't get played once its family got a television. That too, had soothed me, making me forget for a while that Janice Derby was still 'after me'.

But I couldn't ignore the way she had started following me, usually with two or three of her mates. Whenever I turned round in the school playground, she seemed to be there, a sneering, menacing shadow. But the worst times were when I came out of school and had to walk to the butchers or go up to the Co-op, where Mom had, unknown to Granny, opened a 'strap' account.

Then, the group walked almost on my heels, bumping into me on purpose by pushing one another into my back, while all the time Janice's grating voice led the tirade of abuse.

'Cross-eyed, knock-kneed, bow legged - that's YOW, Carol Sheldon!'

'Scared now, aye yer? Yow bay mouthin' off now, bin yer?'

'Yow wull be scared! Jus' wait till Janice gets 'old on yer!'

Shaking in my shoes, trying to outrun my persecutors, I almost wished Janice would beat me up there and then. It would be worth the pain just to get it over with. But my tormentor was obviously enjoying seeing me scwirm!

There seemed to be no-one I could turn to, and I was sitting miserably on the entry wall when my youngest cousin Rose came along.

'Lo, Carol. 'Comin' out?'

It was the time for 'Tin can O'Learky' and 'Release,' two street games I usually loved. But although West Road echoed with the shouts and running feet of my friends, I didn't dare join them. My heart felt as heavy, I thought, turning instinctively to library book land, as poor 'Heidi's' had when she was taken down from the mountain and her beloved Grandfather, and had to sleep on a pillow that felt as if it were full of rocks!

'Nah!' I shook my head as Rose began to inexpertly throw two old tennis balls against the wall. Fairhaired and smaller than me, she suddenly seemed very familiar and comforting, and I found myself blurting out, 'I cor goo in the street, Rosie! Janice Derby's after me!'

Even innocent Rose knew of Janice's reputation. Hastily putting down the balls, she hurried concernedly to my side. 'Tell yer Mom - or yer Nan,' she counselled, putting her small, warm hand on my arm. 'That's wot Ar'd do...'

I looked at her, remembering the way Mom had been since Dad got back from Patsull and started his new job. Christmas seemed like a distant dream, and all I could think of was that she never seemed to stop working nowadays, and though she didn't complain about Granny and Aunt Maud, I knew taking care of them, and us, and the house gave her little time to think of anything else.

'Er'd goo mad if 'er knowed I'd bin swearin' an' shoutin' in the street,' I told Rose, seriously, my face going hot as I recalled the incident which had caused all the trouble. 'An me Nan 'ud be ten times wuss! Ar'll just 'ave ter tek wot's comin' ter me, I s'pose!'

From Aunt Ginny's house, I suddenly heard the signature tune of 'The Archers' wafting through the open window. That was the signal for my cousins to go indoors. A few moments later, I knew my own mother would be on the front doorstep, calling my brother and myself in from the tantalising, now scary twilight.

'Yow could say yer WO fight!' Rose, obviously inspired, turned back to my desolate figure. 'When 'er 'its yer, dow 'it 'er back! That sometimes werks wi' me an' our Joey!'

'Turn the other cheek,' that was called, I ruminated, as I later followed my reluctant brother into the house, and in Aunt Maud's jocular words, 'up the wooden hills to Bedfordshire.' I remembered it from Scripture, when Mrs. Whitecraft sometimes got her favourites to act out Bible stories for the vicar to watch.

The message came, via one of Janice's henchwomen, that she would meet me the following Monday night. To say I was scared was the understatement of the century, and when I came out of school that afternoon, I scarcely noticed that the soft summer rain that brought a harvest of tiny green frogs.

My brother joined other, bigger boys, chasing and throwing them, but their cruelty had little effect on me. Miserably, I put my finger on the beginning of a chalk line that started on the corner of Spring Street and travelled the length of the power station's high wall. 'Follow this line,' was the smudgy instruction. At the end of the line, the words, 'You are saft!' mocked me.

I stared longingly at the smooth sides of the canal 'stepping bridge' where children climbed high to slide down the bannister rail of blue brick that always reminded me of a giant elephant's trunk. I wished I could escape across the bridge, even though I knew it led only to another, larger council estate.

`` Carol!. Wait a bit!' Suddenly Eva and Rose were at my side. 'Our Rosie says yo've bin offered out by Janice Derby!' she said, looking at me, wide eyed with unwitting new respect. 'Er's on'y the Cock o' the street!'

'I know,' I mumbled, aware that Dave and the boys were also taking notice.'It's tonight.'

Later that evening, I stood by our gate waiting for Janice, my heart in my mouth. The word had got round that there was going to be a fight and I had even undergone a kind of training session in the air raid shelter, being told not to bite and scratch like a wench, but to punch er yed, cos her wouldn't be expectin' that.

Now, I looked around to see that the regulation square spaces in the concrete garden walls were full of children, friends and foes, all lined up as if they were in the best seats at the pictures.

As Janice, egged on by her own supporters, towered over me and then struck - a hard blow to my stomach, I gritted my teeth. Resisting what the boys had told me, I thought fixedly of what Rose had said. If I didn't fight back, surely Janice would give up!

Sure enough after the second unreturned body blow, Janice took a step backwards and stared at me.

'Wot's up wi' yer? Think yow'm too good ter fight me?

Winded and dizzy, I looked up into her blurry, malicious face. The puzzlement she couldn't hide was, amazingly, to my advantage. So I stuck my nose in the air, and condescendingly shrugged my shoulders.

Maddened beyond endurance, Janice glanced back over her shoulder to her noisily disappointed mates. 'Why dow yer run ter yer muther - ask 'er wot yer dad was doin' sittin' drinkin' in the pub wi' Eileen Dawson last wick!'

The words hit me harder than any blows could have done. I just stared, open mouthed, while Janice shouted for all to hear about my dad and his fancy woman that she'd heard her mother talking about, over tea.

'Lamp 'er YED, our Carol!' Dave called, as he came from down the entry. And his voice led a sudden roar from the bloodthirsty spectators on the wall. 'If yow dow, I wull!'

In the rage that engulfed me, making me fly at Janice Derby with furious fists and flying feet, I didn't need telling twice!

44

'. . . . *making me fly at Janice Derby with furious fists and flying feet'.*

FIFTEEN

'So now we've got the motor, me an' yer Mom thought we'd like ter tek the kids ter Yorkshire fer a few days - visit 'er sister Annie.'

It was the longest speech I'd ever heard from Grandad and I looked up in surprise from Nan's sofa, where Dave and I sat watching 'Whirlygig.'

Dad had popped in to look at the second hand Austin car that had appeared outside the house. I'd overheard him talking to Mom about US getting a car, too, but the dream had gone the way of the promised television set.

Squirming, I remembered what Aunt Ginny had said about his money, and how Janice's spiteful words about him being in the pub with common Eileen seemed to make sense of it.

'I'll goo an' see what Liza says,' he promised now, as he went towards the verandah door. I longed to go after him, to ask if it were true what Janice's mother had told her, but I knew I didn't dare.

Instead, I tried to concentrate on the avuncular face of Humphrey Lestock on the flickering TV screen, while Nan hurried in from the kitchen, twitching with the excitement of her plans.

'We'll tek yer to see our Annie an' Alf, in Royston,' she said,squeezing down between my brother and me. 'Some o' my brothers am there - workin' down the pit - an' they've mostly got families o' their own be now!'

In spite of my secret anxiety about Dad, I felt my interest rise as I began to realise how much I hoped Mom would say we could go.

The trip was to take place during the last week of July, the first week of the industrial fortnight, when all the factories, including the Austin, closed down. Dave and I were both so excited we couldn't sleep, in spite of the hearth bath, and intensified Friday night purges that we were given. Nan had made us both new flannelette pyjamas, and Aunt Maud supplied her old hop picking suitcase for our few clothes.

'Ere, me babbies, 'ave some spendin' money!' Granny Coley called, busily unflapping her purse before we ran off to where the Austin stood outside our house, while Aunt Maud, beaming, presented us with two apples and two packets of Smiths crisps,.

'Dow ate the blue 'uns! They'm salty!' she repeated the old joke over the visible blue twist of paper which contained the flavouring. We all laughed as if we hadn't heard it before, all except Mom, who suddenly looked anxious, as if realising for the first time that we were really going.

46

` See yer on Sad-dey,` she said, as she awkwardly kissed us both on the cheek, and with a swift glance at Dad, who was hovering in the doorway. 'Be-`arve yerselves, now!`

Head high, I walked down the entry, past the staring Millers, and Eva and Rose who had sneaked out to see us off while their mother watched, a tall shadow behind the net curtains. Did Aunt Ginny know Dad had been in the pub with Eileen Dawson? a little voice asked, tormenting me inside.

'Urry up, our Carol!` Nan`s head poked out through the passenger door and I realised they were all waiting for me.

I had scarcely been out of Tipton before and was quite unprepared for the length of the journey to Yorkshire. The close confines of Grandad`s pride and joy, his first car, made me feel sick, and I swallowed, trying to get rid of the overpowering smell of leather from the shining brown upholstery.

'Open the winder, quick!` Grandad hissed over his shoulder when I eventually confessed how ill I felt. He glanced at Nan, in her Sunday best in the passenger seat,. 'P`raps yo`d berra sit in the back with `em, Soph! An` tek them rags an` perper bags wi` yer, just in case!`

-'Ay we nearly theer, yet?` Dave, untroubled by travel sickness soon got bored and kicked at the seat in front.

'Course we ay!` Nan shot him an exasperated glance as she climbed in between us. 'We`n still got the moors to get across!`

In between bouts of travel sickness, she tried to interest me in the panorama that soon came into view. 'Look over theer, it`s all gold,` she pointed out, 'and in another plerce, it`s all black!`

Grandad explained that the difference in the landscape was due to weather changes, but as I drifted into an exhausted sleep against the bumpy, leathery back seat, all I could think was that we had left the Black Country and were now heading for a country that was shimmering and gold, like I`d read about in 'Pilgrim`s Progress.`

We stayed in Royston for four days with Nan`s sister and brother in law in a tiny colliery house that seemed packed with people. 'This is your cousin, Betty,` Aunt Annie introduced me to a girl of about 12 and her brother, Max, who was nearer my own age. 'You`ll be sharing t`back bedroom.`

Later, Betty led me up the steep, narrow stairs to a room divided by a floral curtain. 'T`lads`ll be behind theer!` she said, then looking at me curiously.'D`yer live with yer Gramma, then?

47

``No.` I sat down cautiously on the edge of the feather bed the two of us would share. It seemed strange to hear Nan called `Gramma,` though I supposed that`s what she was. `My Mom an` Dad couldn`t come,` I explained, smoothing the ruffled satin eiderdown.` They `ave to look after my other Granny an` Auntie, an` they ay safe to be left.`

`Oh.` Betty gave a little shrug. `Let`s go and get some spice,` she said, mysteriously. `We can save it up for when they`ve all got to t`club.`

-`Haven`t you ever heard of sugar and spice an` all things nice?` Betty`s dad breathed beerily over me later that night when the grown up returned noisily from their evening out.

We had passed the time sharing the sweets Betty and Max had taken us to the corner shop to buy. Much to my delight, we had also had singing and dancing, especially when Sheila and Jeffrey, two children from next door had come in.

`Sheila and Jeffrey live on their own with their Mam!` Betty whispered confidentially, as we settled down on the snowy white bolster together. `Their dad ran off last year with his fancy woman!`

SIXTEEN

My head was filled to bursting with all the new sights and sounds I had encountered in Yorkshire. But as the Austin took us home to Tipton, all I could think of was would Dad still be there - or would he have run off with Eileen Dawson?

'Yow'm quiet, our Carol,' Nan noticed, from the passenger seat. 'Not feelin' sick again, am yer?'

I shook my head. 'Just thinkin' about gooin' um,' I said, more gloomily than I intended.

'Er's SCARED!' my brother piped up knowingly as she fidgeted with his woolly socks by my side. 'Er 'ad a big fight wi' Janice Derby an' Janice sed er'd kill 'er, next time!'

Luckily, Nan was too busy pointing out the passing scenery again to really take in what he'd said. Giving him a surreptitious kick, I closed my eyes, reliving the moment when, sore but unbloodied, I'd emerged from my battle with Janice.

'Dow think yow've WON!' she spat, as the shouts of the audience told me that, amazingly, I'd done just that. 'Cos I'll KILL yer what I see yer again!'

Just then, one of the quieter of our neighbours had walked past on her way home from weekly choir practice, and Janice had turned, sobbing piteously, in her direction:

'Oh, Mrs. Plant!' she wailed. 'Carol Sheldon swore at me an' - an' now er's 'it me really 'ard!'

There, in the back seat of Grandad's car, I went hot with shame again, and my eyes filled with tears. As I relived Mrs Plant's shocked response.

'CAROL!' Horrified, she took in Janice's punched, and snotty face; the dishevelled state of our clothes and the spectators, still baying for blood on the council street walls. 'And I thought you were such a REFINED little girl!' she said, before going, with a sorrowfully shaking head, on her way down the street.

It was then that I'd succumbed to tears, running indoors and straight up to bed to sob myself to sleep.

It was dark by the time we reached West Road that night. As soon as Grandad stopped the car I was out and running up the entry to the ever open back door.

'Where's Dad?' I panted, looking all round.

Mom stared at me. 'Come in like yerself,' she said. "Ad a nice time,'ave yer?'and as I again asked my fearfilled question. 'Yer dad's doin' some overtime, but 'e'll be back any minute.' she broke off and peered at me suspiciously. 'Why?'

'I...' Relief flooded through me, making me realise how tired I was, and also how glad, in spite of everything, to be home. 'I jus' want to tell 'im about Yorkshire,' I lied, running back to the door where Nan and Grandad were struggling in with the suitcases and Dave was jumping up and down in his eagerness to see Mom. 'We went over t'moors, an' 'ad spice, an' slep' in Betty and Max's room, an' went to the Salvation Army on Sundey, an' the pictures on Sad-dey afternoon!'

'Calm down, yow'll werk the 'ousehold up!' Smiling in spite of herself, Mom put her work reddened hand on my shoulder, and drew Dave closer into a hug.

As Nan and Grandad told her all the news from Royston, who had married, who'd had babbies, I was able to return in my imagination to the wonderful film we had seen with our new found cousins.

'Singin' in the rain! I'm 'Singin' in the rain!' As I sang the words in my head, I mentally joined Gene Kelly in his amazing, long distance tap dance to the lamp-post shower. It felt even better than being a Carrol Levis Discovery, and I couldn't wait for our next concert in the entry of 3, West Road.

But first, I had to face up to the retribution promised me by Janice Derby, and, more important, to find out if what she'd said about my father was true.

SEVENTEEN

`On the wall, you will see a picture.` Mrs. Whitecraft nodded her severe head towards the dunces side of the class. The picture was directly above me - a picture of a boy with a toy sailing boat and behind him, a stretch of blue water. `You are to write a composition about the things you see in that picture.`

I breathed out in deep satisfaction as the familiar, tingling excitement seeped into my bones. For the time it took to write the composition, I could escape the stuffy classroom where I now sat next to Wilfred Miller.

I could be with the boy and the sailboat. The boat might get lost, I thought, as I picked up my scratchy school pen, and dipped it into the inkwell. Or maybe the boy had just been given it as a present.......

Wilfred, who was thin and sly looking, with curling black hair, was shuffling at my side, fiddling around with the inkwell. And then, I heard Mrs. Whitecraft's voice again:

`Carol Sheldon! I trust you are not putting PAPER into that inkwell!`

`NO, Miss!` Even though I was innocent, hating the way the white enamel inkwells became clogged, I still went hot all over. I was aware that all the class was staring, and waves of disapproval were coming from the top end where Mary and Pamela were eager to start the project.

Mrs. Whitecraft picked up the inkwell, examined it, and my heart sank. There was no way I could `tell` on Wilfred.

`I think YOU'D better go and stand in the corridor!` the teacher said, plucking me triumphantly from my seat. `Go on! We can do without trouble makers in this class!`

`But....!` As Wilfred Miller smirked, I left the class and went to stand outside, where I knew, sinkingly, that I would soon fall prey to Mr. Lodge. It wasn't fair, I ruminated. All I'd really wanted to do was write about the boy and his boat. As the door of the study opened and the stern headmaster came out and began to stride, glaringly towards me, I consoled myself with one thought.

Eventually the school day would end. I'd go home and sit by the fire with my red notebook at the indelible pencil that wrote blue when you licked it. Nothing on earth would be able to stop me writing the story then!

When I did get home that day, I was sent straight out again to buy some Fennings Fever Mixture for Granny Coley who had been `took bad.`

`It`ll bring yer temperature down, Gran!` Mom argued when Granny vehemently protested from her bed that she didn`t want that `bitter tastin` muck.` She paused as she straightened the eiderdown over the frail body. `If yow dow, yow`ll `ave to `ave one of Big Ginny`s kaolin poultices - or send fer the doctor!`

`No doctor comin` `ere - an` as fer Ginny - er cun use `er poultices on `er gob!` the old woman muttered, then, turning to me: `Goo on then, Cock - fetch the Fennings, an` ave a penny outta the change fer some suck!`

`Spice.` I said to myself, as I hurried through the back door. Our time in Yorkshire seemed an age and a world away and I tried to imagine what Betty and Max were doing now, while in the background the abandoned Sheila and Jeffrey still hovered. A reminder of the insecurity I carried around with me - and the promise I had made to get to the bottom of it.

When I got back with the medicine, Granny seemed much worse, thrashing around in her bed and mumbling about someone called `Old un!`

`That`s wot `er called `er `usband. `E got burnt ter jeth in the pit.` Mom told me anxiously. `Goo an` fetch yer aunt Ginny - er`ll know wot ter do!`

Not needing to be told twice, I ran round to Big Aunt Ginny`s where as usual all the children were in the back kitchen while their father ate his supper in splendid isolation in the front room.

`Mom says can yer goo in ter Gran - `er`s delirious,` I said, surprising myself and them with a new word I`d recently picked up from a book.

Aunt Ginny was out of the back door in a flash, her outsize apron flapping round her, and her big hands bunched into fists. `I tode yer muther `er wor well days agoo!` she called accusingly over her shoulder.

Taken aback, I stood for a moment, looking around me. Brenda was washing her long, dark hair in the sink, the smell of `Drene` shampoo all around her. Eva sat embroidering, something she seemed to do a lot of since her mother told me, triumphantly she had `become a woman` and wouldn`t be coming out to play so much

The boys, Joey and Terry were sorting through a pile of ancient Dandy and Beano comics on the hearth, and Rose? Rose was sitting under the table crying her eyes out!

`What`s up, Rose?` Nobody moved as I got down on all fours and, moving across the newspaper that served as a weekday tablecloth, crawled under to join her. `Wot yer blartin` for?`

'I AY!' Rose protested, but her face was bleary and smeared with tears and snot, and she couldn't deny it for long. 'Our mother's 'it me!' she finally burst out, as I handed her the hankie rag that, though unhemmed, my mother always made sure was clean.'Er sed I'm disgruced the fam'ly!'

'Disgruced?' I squatted beside her, the legs of table, chairs, and children hemming us securely in from all sides.

'DISGRACED, yer saft bugger!' Dropping her embroidery with her mysterious new found 'womanhood', Eva fell onto her knees to join us.

'Yo' know the nit nuss come to yore school terday?' she whispered, 'Well, our Rose got gid a NOTE!'

I stared, horrified, remembering the struggle Mom had, week after week, keeping my brother and myself free of head lice. Anything to prevent the frequently visting 'nit nurse' from giving us a note to take home to our parents. Those who WERE given notes were secretly shunned, looked down upon as Mr Lodge had encouraged us to look down on the boys with impetigo.

As far as I knew, nobody in our family had come home with a 'note' and that included all Aunt Ginny's brood.

'Wot meks it wuss, though,' Eva went on, as Rose, mortified, moaned aloud and covered her hot and sticky face with her hands. 'Wot meks it wuss is our Rose cum all down the street - an' up the entry ' all excited - shoutin' 'Mom! Mom! The NURSE 'as sent yer a letter! Our muther nearly killed her!'

EIGHTEEN

The doctor said Granny Coley should be kept in bed and given 'slops.' I no longer overheard her and Aunt Maud grumbling in the night, though the snores were just as bad.

Aunt Maud had, in fact, begun to 'wander off', tramping the streets with the rain making her white hair go frizzy and an umbrella forgotten in the bottom of her big black shopping bag. She began to talk about a daughter I didn't know she had, and one day the daughter, Elsie, came to visit.

'I thought I'd berra come an' see Gran,' she whispered, meaningfully as Mom showed her through the gleaming front room and up the stairs. When she came down, she was shaking her smart, bubble cut perm and dabbing her eyes with a snowy handkerchief. 'She dow look too good ter me, Liza,' she said to Mom and, taking the cup of tea she was handed. 'Er - yow an' my mother? Yer gerron well together, dow yer?'

There was a moment's silence as Mom finished wiping the draining board and putting the cosy over the teapot. Then Mom turned and met the other woman's rather shifty gaze. 'Ar, we do, Elsie,' she said clearly, suddenly looking taller and more in control than I had ever seen her. 'But that dow mean I want 'er ter live wi' me forever. When anythin' 'appens ter Gran, I think it'll be yore place to tek yer muther, dow yow?'

Dad was at home, breaking wood in the coal hole and as Elsie flushed and nodded and said OF COURSE Aunt Maud should end her days with her, I saw him poke out his head and meet Mom's suddenly brave green eyes. Neither said a word but the look that passed between them spoke volumes.

That night, nobody seemed to bother to call us in from our play in the street and Eva, Rose and I took advantage of the extra time by inviting all the Miller children to watch us sing and dance.

A captive audience behind the wooden palings, they fidgeted or stared, and made rude noises while Eva and I did our famous interpretation of 'I'll be with you in Appleblossom Time.'

Rose still seemed downcast, and I somehow found myself sitting by her on the damp back step long after the Millers had escaped the concert and gone indoors.

'There's somewheer important I've got to goo, soon,' I heard myself say, confidingly. 'Yow c'n come wi' me, if yow like, Rosie - soo long as yow swear ter keep it a secret!'

Eva and I did our famous interpretation of 'I'll be with you in Apple Blossom Time'.

My plan was to follow Dad next time he got all dressed up and went out in the evening. Then I'd know for sure if the whispers I'd heard about him and Eileen were true. I didn't know what, if any, action would come next, but just making a decision helped me feel better.

As Eva appeared, with strict instructions from Aunt Ginny that it was time to go in, I gave Rose a knowing look and made my own way indoors. Mom looked as if she'd been crying, and she told Dave and I that Granny was even worse.

'So be good kids 'an stay from under me feet, these next few days,' she requested.

'Is Granny gonna die?' My brother asked as we got into our lumpy bed together.

'I dow know!' I snapped. 'Er's very ode, ay 'er?'

Long after he'd gone to sleep I lay awake listening to the footsteps going back and forth into Granny's room. I tried to imagine dying - not being able to get your breath, or eat anything but the 'slops' - bread and milk, weak tea and 'oxo' which were all the doctor said Granny should be given.

Then I thought of Aunt Maud sleeping with her sick mother, as she had done every night I could remember. What if she woke up in the morning and Granny was lying beside her, DEAD?

The only dead thing I'd ever seen was the day old chick Dave and I got off the rag and bone man when we were much younger. It seemed very sick, and cold, and so we'd put it under the tea cosy on the warm grate. When Mom had lifted the cosy sometime later, she'd screamed, and the chicken had fallen out, dead.

Fitfully, I tossed and turned, and finally fell asleep to dream I was being chased by a big yellow chicken with Janice Derby's face.

NINETEEN

When I got home from school next day there was a small crowd of neighbours and passers by standing by our gate.

'It's GRANNY!' Rose said, wonderingly, at my side. 'Look - in the upstairs winder!'

We stood unnoticed and stared with the passers by as, through the open window, a scrawny arm waved a white handkerchief, Then Granny Coley's plaintive but still frantic voice blasted over our heads:

'MURDER! Fetch somebody! They'm bloody clammin' me in 'ere! Tryin' ter kill me off in me own wum!'

'Slops!' I told the nearest figure, and my face went hot as I saw it was Mrs Plant, who had seen the aftermath of my battle with Janice. At the same time, restraining hands were seen taking Granny from the window and firmly closing it.

The crowd quickly dispersed, but indoors, the shame had only just begun. Mom, her lips tight, had run round to Big Aunt Ginny's and was in the middle of asking : 'Wot'll I do with 'er, Ginny? Yo' eard the doctor say nuthin' solid cos of 'er age an' state o' health....'

'Huh!' My great aunt cocked her head to where the sound of Granny's hungry lament was coming through her own open window,.'Ark at that! There ay much wrong wi' 'er state o' health now, is there?'

For the first time ever, I thought I saw a glimpse of something like compassion in her gaunt face as she looked at my mother's anxious one. 'Ar'll tell yer wot ter do wi' 'er, Liza,' she said, rolling up her sleeves to tackle the pile of potatoes waiting to be peeled by the stone sink. 'Gi' 'er sum eggs an' baercon - a big plaertful! It'll either kill or cure 'er!'

By the next morning, Granny Coley seemed like her old self again, insisting on coming downstairs to sit by the fire while Mom went about her jobs.

'Ar, I bin poorly, Grainger,' she told the old lady neighbour who looked in to see her with a bottle of stout. 'One stage I day know whether I was on this earth or Fullers! But our Liza looked after me! Er's allus bin a golden wench ter me, an' allus wull be!'

Hunched over the stove, Mom seemed to be crying again. I went over and asked her worriedly what was wrong, but she just shook her head and turned away. 'Goo an' spend yer pocket money. I'll be all right in a bit,' she said.

On my way to Sid Tarr's, clutching the two brown pennies Granny had given me, I pondered on the strangeness of grown ups. Mom had cried when Granny had been going to die; now Granny was better she was still crying.

And things weren't getting any better with Dad. He and Mom had a terrible row the night before. I'd heard things falling over when he came home very late obviously from the pub, and Mom had been 'shushing' him until finally her voice was raised with his, and I'd lain in bed wondering where it was all going to end.

'Oi! Carol Sheldon! Ar've bin lookin ' fer YOW!' Everything seemed to freeze inside me at the now familiar taunting voice coming from behind me as I reached the corner. I stopped and turned and was face to face with Janice Derby. 'Jus' thought yow'd like ter know I'm still after yer!' she called, as her cronies gathered round her like a flock. 'Dow think yow scared me, jus' cos yow lost yer rag about her dad's fancy 'ooman! I c'n still gi' yow wot for!'

'Oh ar? 'Dimly, I saw that I too had been joined - by my brother, by Rose and Joey and Terry, whose slightly taller presence suddenly gave me new courage. 'Come on then!' I challenged, scarcely aware that my little group was making encouraging noises. Only aware that Janice, after taking one step towards me, was miraculously backing off!

'Oh - I cor be bothered!' she finally said, shrugging exaggeratedly. 'Yow ay wuth fightin' anyroadup!'

'Frightened o' gerrin another lampin', Janice?' Dave cupped his hands round his mouth and yelled after Janice's retreating back. 'My sister'll bost yer YED in!'

Meanwhile, flushed with success and wanting only to sort out the other main problem in my life, I took Rose quickly to one side. 'We'll goo ter that secret plearce tonight,' I decided. 'I'll meet yer in the entry at six. Aw right?'

Deciding how much to tell Rose was a problem, but in the end I didn't have to say much at all.

'Foller yer DAD?' she echoed, staring at me, eyes wider than ever. 'Is it like 'ide 'n' seek?'

'A bit.' Before I came into the entry, Dad had been busy at the sink, brylcreeming his dark hair and cocking his head to one side to get the parting right. He wore a clean white shirt and his one and only tie, a narrow striped one Nan had given him for Christmas.

Soon, Rose and I heard the sound of the back door shutting, followed by his faint but unmistakable whistle. 'Quick - throw me the ball.!' I hissed to Rose. Startled, she obeyed, and I caught the old tennis ball just as Dad reached us.

``Avin` fun, kids?' he said, preoccupied, stopping for a mere second to look at us. I threw the ball back to Rose. 'Ar. Wheer yer gooin`, Dad?'

Dad was nearly by the gate. He didn't look back at me as he said: 'On`y fer a pint, Cock, - prob`ly at the Crown.' Then, almost as an afterthought, he went on: 'Yow be good fer yer muther. Goo in when `er calls `yer!'

'Right. Come on!' Pushing the ball into the pocket of my Coronation dress, I grabbed Rose`s hand. By the time Dad had turned the corner of West Road and was heading towards Ocker Hill we were hot on his trail, careful to duck behind the solid garden walls if he showed the slightest sign of turning round.

'It IS like `ide `n` seek!' Rose giggled as we stood in Jimmy Tarr`s entrance and watched Dad turn towards Gospel Oak. He seemed to be hurrying now, obviously late for whoever he had to see.

One thing was certain, I realised, my heart falling like a stone. He definitely WASN`T going to the 'Crown and Cushion' for a pint!

TWENTY

'I cor goo along the CUT, Carol!' Rose plucked nervously at my arm as I tried to lead her in the direction Dad had gone when he finally left Gospel Oak road. 'Our Mom's allus tode me to keep away from the cut!' she explained, agitatedly. 'If ever 'er fun out....!'

'Er WO!' Beginning to regret my decision to bring Rose, I looked fixedly at the purposeful figure now some way ahead of us on the canal towpath. Dad was heading towards a distant bridge and if he decided to climb back up to the road from there, I knew we'd lose him altogther.

'Look - we'll turn round an' goo 'um soon - honest!' I told the still wavering Rose. 'But let's jus' see wheer 'e's gooin - okay?'

'Okay.' Rose sighed and followed me through the brambles and down onto the quiet towpath. The canal gleamed, deep and mysterious waters lapping its brick sides in the quickly gathering twilight. There were bulrushes among which I knew the ducks had roosted for the night.

As Rose and I ran towards the looming bridge, I suddenly realised I wasn't at all sure where we were anymore, and, more important, I had no idea what time it was! Under the bridge, a humped shape against the dank and dripping wall parted at the sound of our flapping footsteps. And became a man and a woman.

'Bloody kids - gerrout of 'ere!' The man's snarl was nothing like my dad's voice and I breathed a sigh of relief. As Rose and I blundered past, splashing in the puddles that had settled beneath the bridge's iron awning, the woman struck a match to light a cigarette, and I saw, to my utter amazement, that it was Mavis Derby - Janice's mother!

'I thought that'd be Eileen Dawson!' I said to the breathless Rose. Some instinct told me not to mention that I'd also feared the male figure was my Dad. Realising he must have disappeared into one of the pubs along the main road, I took her hand and we began to run home. The sky was still light, but I knew it was way past our time to be called indoors.

'It's a quarter to nine, Cock!' a man coming out of the Crown and Cushion answered my apprehensive question sometime later. Rose started to cry then, and I stopped running long enough to shake her.

'Stop blartin'!' I ordered, now wishing with all my heart I had gone on my desperate mission alone. 'They might not even've missed we, yert!'

60

But we both knew that was a very vain hope. Even before we turned the corner into West Road, we heard the voices, many and varied:

'Car-ul! Wheer am yer?

'Rose! Rose! Come in, Rose! Yer muther waents yer!'

The figures searching the gardens were illuminated in the opaquely dying summer light. By the front gate, where she was scarcely ever seen, Big Aunt Ginny stood, arms folded across her ample bosom, silent with anticipation and fury.

'My kids KNOW they cum in after the Archers!' she muttered. 'Our Rosie's fell under a bad influence ternight - er's very easy led, is our babby!'

I had time to register that the person she was talking to was my mother, who stood, rigid with shame and anger, at her side. Then, Rose was flinging herself at Big Aunt Ginny's apron front, sobbing:

'Oh, Mom - it wort me! It wuz Carol! 'Er took me off, along the cut!'

'The CUT? Wot did I tell yer!' The crow was in the look as well as in the shocked and victorious voice of Big Ginny. I hung back, uncertain and terrified as Rose's sisters and brothers joined their mother and they bore her, still wailing, up the entry and into the safety of the house.

Then, it was just me and Mom, with her flashing green eyes and clenched mouth, and a moment later, hard blows, raining down on me. 'Wot 'd yer goo OFF for, eh? Frightenin' the life out of everybody!'

I covered my face with my hands, my heart was in my mouth and I couldn't speak, even if I'd had the words. The force of her angry hands propelled me along the echoeing entry and round the corner into our back kitchen.

'An' wot did yer 'tice ROSE off, for?' She shouted the name as she chased me, knocking over chairs, and falling down on the polished lino. Suddenly, illuminatingly, I knew she was doing this for Big Aunt Ginny's benefit - making sure that Rose's irate mother knew I was getting the punishment I deserved.

'You GOAT!' she screamed,. oblivious to the startled noises coming from the old ladies' bedroom. 'I'll learn yer ter do as yow'm tode!'

Thrusting me up the stairs, she pushed me through the bedroom door to where my brother, eyes like saucers, lay cowering in our bed. As the purposeful fists came, agonisingly, on my bare arms and legs, I suddenly found my voice. Knowing it was the only way to make her stop:

'I 'ad ter foller Dad! They say 'e's bin meeting Eileen Dawson!'

TWENTY ONE

`Eileen Dawson? Why should I be meetin` Eileen Dawson? I`m married ter YOW, ay I?`

Dad`s frenzied voice echoed through the house and I drew nearer to Dave for comfort. I ached all over from the beating my mother had given me and my eyes felt raw from crying.

As Mom, crying too, told Dad all she had extracted from me about the rumours I`d heard, I actually heard Dad laugh. But it was a sad and bitter sounding laugh.

`An` yo`d rather believe kids tittle tattle than yer own `usband! `Onest ter God, Liza, I may`ve SPOKE to Eileen a couple o` times - er tried ter get a bit pally when I was fust outta the `ospital, an` I DID buy `elf `alf pint one Friday in the `Cup`. But as fer anythin` else, it`s all bloody lies!`

`Well I DOW BELIEVE YER!` Mom`s reply carried, with her running feet, up the stairs, and I covered my face with the sheet. It was all like a nightmare, and the worst thing was knowing it was all my fault!

By the time Dave and I woke up that Sunday morning, the house was ominously silent. There was none of the usual smell of weekend cooked breakfast, and only Aunt Maud around, washing crocks from the night before.

`Mother`s still asleep,` she said, `soo I thought I`d gerrup and mek a start. I`ve done plenty o` washing up at the glassworks, ay I?`

I nodded and she peered at me. `Wot`s up wi` yer ferce, Cocker? It`s all red an` blotchy!`

`Er`s bin cryin` cos our Mom lamped`er last night,` Dave replied, and then, looking around. `Wheer`s Mom gone?`

Aunt Maud shrugged her boney shoulders. `Gone a nuttin`!` she joked. Then, `Gone to see `Eileen` I `eard `er say`.

Fear clutched me. What if Mom had gone to hit Eileen the way she`d hit me? Somebody might call the police, and she`d be taken to prison! Numb with terror, I found a corner of the kitchen and just sat there, not even tempted out by the Weetabix and hot milk that Aunt Maud was making for our breakfast.

Nan would be expecting us for our usual Sunday visit, and I longed to be there, sitting on her old sofa, her arms wrapped round me for our five minutes love. I closed my eyes, reliving the warm, encouraging things she'd told me about how Mom and Dad had got to know each other.

'Proper child'ood sweet'arts, they was,' she recounted, clucking at the affectionate remembrance. 'In the serm class at skule an' everythin'. When they come to be married, yer muther day 'ave a penny to 'er nerm - bein' brought up by 'er ode Gran, an' all, so I set to an' med 'er frock an' 'er was the loveliest bride that ever walked down the aisle o' St Mark's church - an' the most pure!'

I wasn't quite sure what 'pure' meant, though I'd heard it in reference to the Virgin Mary in our Catechism lessons at school, and it vaguely tied up in my mind with Lux toilet soap which my mother always insisted on using on her face instead of 'Sunlight.'

A knock at the door startled me back to reality and a moment later, Terry and Joey came in to call for Dave. 'I've gorra set o' wheels in the shelter - fer the trolley!' the older boy said, as my brother hastily finished gulping down his breakfast and fastened the clasp of his striped elasticated 'snake belt.' He shot me a knowing look before saying to Aunt Maud. 'Dow worry, I wo' tek 'im off anywheer...'

A moment later, Joey was poking his tousled head round the door. 'Yer Nan's comin'!' he told me, his voice full of gleeful foreboding. But the words were music to my eyes, as was the sound of Nan calling anxiously:

'Lize? 'Arold? Why ay the kids cum down this mornin'? Me an' Grandad's bin worried...!'

As she entered the room, I flew at her much as Rose had flown at Big Aunt Ginny the night before, hiding my face in her warm side as fresh tears poured out of me.

'Why, wot on earth's the marrer, our Carol?'

Before I could reply, Aunt Maud, on her way back upstairs with a brown paper bag full of pears, said: ''Er mother's lamped 'er! Dow know wot for! I'll just goo 'n' see if Mom's awake.'

Nan stared at me before taking me to the sofa by the unlit grate. 'Now, tell me all about it,' she urged. 'As yer Mom really set about yer, or is yer ferce just red from cryin'?'

'I....'Torn between loyalty to Mom and the need to confess the terrible trouble I'd caused, I gulped and was unable to say anything except that I'd been punished for taking Rose off along the canal.

Just then, there came the sound of heavy footsteps coming down the stairs and to my amazement, Dad stood in the doorway with the suitcase he'd taken to hospital in his hand. He looked very pale and grim and he hadn't shaved. He didn't even glance in my direction as he said:

'I'm glad yow'm 'ere, mother. I was just comin' down wum ter see yer.'

'An' why've yer got the suitcase, our 'Arold?' Nan held me tighter as she stared across at him. In answer, Dad sighed and glanced around him in the trapped way I'd seen before.

'Me and Liza ay gorra bi' o' peace in this plerce,' he said. 'It's all werk 'an' sleep, an' now the Lost City bastards've spread it round that I'm seein' another 'ooman! Turnin' me own kids aginst me!'

As his eyes finally met mine, I realised he wasn't angry with me at all, but at the people who had gossiped behind our backs. I longed to run to him, but his next words held me fast to Nan's side.

'So I've decided, our Mom., I'm gerrin outa 'ere, right now! I'm coming back ter live we' yow an' Dad, wheer I belong!'

'AM yer, now?' Easing me gently to one side, Nan got up and walked over to where Dad stood, the suitcase at his feet. 'Well, I've got news fer yow, our 'Arold,' she said, her tone very measured and straight, so that each word met its target, 'Yow can allus come an' visit, an' wot me an' yer dad can do fer yer, we allus wull. But as fer leavin' Liza an' yer children, that's another matter entirely! Yow've med yer bed, my lad, and now yow must lie on it!'

TWENTY TWO

Mom had come in so quietly none of us heard her. But when I turned and saw her, I caught my breath because she looked so beautiful! Gone was the habitual scarf turban and smudgy apron. She wore her best frock, black crepe with cream inserts in the bodice, and her dark hair was rolled and pinned into curls around her head.

'Lize...' Dad took a step towards her, and I knew that, like me, he was fearful of what she was about to say or do. Wordlessly, Mom went across to the stove and poured herself a cup of tea from the perpetually stewing pot. She stood nursing it, as she looked from Dad to Nan to me. Instinctively, I drew closer to Nan, torn between love and the new fear that the thrashing of the night before had woken in me.

But Nan suddenly moved away: 'Hark!' she said, going towards the stairs. 'I think I 'ear Maud, shoutin' we. I'll goo up and see wot 'er wants..'

After Nan had gone, Mom seemed to find it easier to talk. She drained the cup and put it in the sink. Then, she turned and faced Dad.

'It's awright, 'Arold,'she said, quietly.' I've bin ter ferce yer fancy woman!'

Dad drew in his breath. 'Ow many times do I 'ave ter tell yer, 'er AY!' he began.

'I wanted to 'ear it from 'er!' Mom went on, evenly. 'Soo I gorrup early, got meself dolled up an' walked round to East Road.'

'Wait a bit...' Dad shot a look in my direction. 'Goo an' find yer Nanna,. Carol,' he instructed.

Responding to the warmth in his voice, I got to my feet, but Mom held up a hand which stopped me in my tracks 'No. I want 'er to 'ear this, 'Arold, as 'er's the one that 'ad to purrup with all the talk!' .

Mom took a step towards me, and I instinctively moved back. 'Dow worry, Cock,' she whispered, and I saw the glint of tears in her eyes. 'I wo' it yer again - EVER again, if I c'n 'elp it! I just want yer to know, it is all lies about yer Dad an' that Eileen Dawson.'

She broke off, and smiled crookedly in Dad's direction. 'Er as good as tode me yo was too ode! Er might've tried to gerroff wi' yer once, an' let yer pay for 'alf pint o' mild one night. But 'er's got other fish ter fry, an' yo ay a patch on 'er new bloke - from Wensbury!'

'She wore her best frock, black crepe with cream inserts . . . .'

It felt as if a great weight had been lifted off my chest. As the back door opened and Dave, Joey and Terry came in with the buckled wheels of an old pram for Dad to mend, Mom put the kettle on again.

She and Dad sat down with their tea at the table and I knew without being told that now was the time for me to go about my own business. I'd go upstairs to my current library book, though it was a pity it was 'Black Beauty'. I'd cried so much over the past twenty four hours I didn't really want to cry anymore.

Upstairs, the house was cold, the stairs leading straight down to the front door, which was invariably left open. It was quiet, too, just the hum of Nan's voice, carrying on some sort of monologue from the old ladies' bedroom.

I was glad of the quiet after all the quarrels. It gave me an opportunity to think about all that had happened, starting with me beating Janice Derby and ending with Mom beating me. I knew that once I started to think, I'd start to write in the red notebook, and that whatever the story that came out, it would give me comfort, just as Nan's old fashioned Netherton stories always did.

'-Nan!' My grandmother herself appeared so suddenly out of the dark bedroom in front of me I almost fell down the stairs. Her face looked different, somehow, set and strange,and she moved distractedly past me. 'Not now, cock,' she said, over her shoulder as she hurried down the stairs. 'I've gorra see yer mother!'

I followed her instinctively back down and as the living room door opened, saw that Mom and Dad stood in each other's arms by the firegrate. Locked like the childhood sweethearts they used to be.

They only turned away from each other when Nan said, quietly, from the doorway:

'I think yow'd best send fer Ginny, my wench. Yowr Gran's passed away.'

The day of the funeral, Mom sat in the back kitchen and cried and people kept coming and telling her she had nothing to reproach herself with. `Yow did yer dooty by `er, cocker - nobody con say any diff`runt!`

Sent out to play, Dave and I kept sneaking back to be fed ham sandwiches and slices of Nan`s fruit cake. Nobody had suggested we go to the church. Instead, we had been left in the care of Mrs. Grainger who had `laid Granny out` and was also in charge of the spread.

`Yow`d never`d believed Coley was ninety one - er was in real good nick!` I overheard her telling another woman as they sliced and buttered bread in the crowded kitchen. `It was all I cud do ter shut `er eyes wi` the pennies.`

`Why`d yer do that, Mrs. Grainger?` I asked, nosily, by her elbow. She started, pulling a warning face at her companion who murmured something about `little pitchers` and `big handles`.

`Why, so`s God con open their eyes agen in `eaven o` course!` she said. `An` we use pennies cos they`m `eavy!`

As I wandered away, I thought of the pennies Granny Coley had pressed into our hands over the years. Heavy, cold coins that had soon grown hot and wet from our perspiration, staining our hands as we hurried up the hill to what waited in Sid Tarr`s suck shop.

I remembered how, the night before, I`d lain bed awake long after my brother was asleep, listening to Aunt Maud talking to herself in the room she used to share with Granny.

`I`m gooin` to our Elsie`s, yer know,` she`d told me, yesterday, matter of factly. `So yow be a good little wench, after I`ve gone.`

`I will, Aunt Maud.` I`d hugged her boney bulk a bit awkwardly. `but I`ll miss yer!` I`d added, truthfully.

`Ah well.` The old lady pushed back my hair in an almost motherly gesture. `Yowr Mom an` Dad deserve ter be on their own now - an` besides, it ay the serm `ere - not now mother`s gone...`

-`Our mother says yow`ll prob`ly ALL `ave ter leave now!` As I wandered into the front room, shining with all Mom`s extra efforts, I thought of something Eva had said, when we gathered in the air raid shelter to talk about Granny Coley`s death. `Yer dad`s name AY in the rent book, like I tode yer!`

Anxiety jabbed at me. It felt as if everything in the world was changing and I didn't know how to respond. If only I could go back to when Granny was still here, an aged but solid shape in the candle light. But to do that would be to return to the time when Mom and Dad weren't happy and I seemed to be carrying the burden of the rumours about him and Eileen Dawson all on my own.

The 'spread' gradually disappeared into hungry mouths, and the beer the men had fetched from the off licence was poured into our few drinking glasses. Big Aunt Ginny and Mom worked for once side by side at both the kitchen table and the sink. They were standing at the sink when Granny Coley's long lost son, Gerald, came in and kissed Mom:

'Just as lovely as ever, I see, our young Liza!' he said, appreciatively. 'No wonder our mother thought the world on yer!'

To his sister Ginny, he barely nodded and after he'd passed, she turned to Mom, with a look that didn't try to hide her jealousy and spite.

'What yer gonna do now then, Lize?' she asked, craftily.' Move in an' lodge wi' 'Arold's mother?'

-'Not bloody likely!' Shocked, I turned to see Nan, stately in her black funeral coat, bearing down on Big Aunt Ginny.

Nan smelt as if she'd had a glass or two of the stout that was now being dished out in the front room. She pushed her way past Ginny and stood resolutely at Mom's side.

'Our Liza's gorra perfectly good wum 'ere - one 'er's worked damned 'ard for!' she said, as those nearest gave a small cheer. 'We'm off ter the Municipal Buildings furst thing on Monday mornin' an' if they dow gi' our 'Arold the tenancy - I - I'll chain meself ter the railin's!'

It was twelve months after Granny Coley's death and Mom had finally found somebody to exchange council houses with us so that we could leave the Lost City.

'It's a woman 'oo's mother lives in South Road, an' 'er wants to be nearer 'er,' she had explained, when she came back from one of her regular visits to the municipal buildings with a white card. 'Oh 'Arold, let's goo an' look at 'er 'ouse in Central Avenue - see if we can swap.'she pleaded. 'The kids am gerrin bigger now, an' I dow want 'em growin' up round 'ere!'

I frowned, thinking of the rag and bone men, the kids who threw stones in the summer and ice packed snowballs in the winter. The dogs that hung, half starved, around the gardens which were sometimes invaded by the rag and bone men's horses in the middle of the night

'I allus 'ad it 'ard,' Mom admitted, as she sipped the bottle of Guiness Dad had started bringing her as a tonic, from his less frequent visits to the pub. 'I want things ter be berra fer them!'

The new house was still in Tipton, at a place called Princes End. Dave and I hadn't seen it yet, but Mom and Nan were both excited and scandalized by the fact that it was 'manky'!

'Never mind, we'll soon 'ave it claened!' Nan said, coming to see us with a pile of empty soap powder boxes from the Co-op. 'Though 'ow Ginny'll like ER new neighbours, I shouldn't like ter say! They seem pretty riffy ter me!'

Big Aunt Ginny, tight lipped, asked no questions and heard no lies. But the day the removal van arrived to move us out, she arranged to have a big load of coal delivered, right across the front gateway.

''Ow'll I get to school?' I asked, as we climbed over the coal to help the removal men with our few things. 'Is the new 'ouse a long way from St. Mark's?'

My dad put his arm around me, and warmth and life flowed between us with the love that had no need of words. 'We'll get yer theer,' he promised, and then, as if struck by a sudden, illuminating thought, he threw back his head, and laughed. 'Hey, Carol. I ay tode yer Mom yet, but this plerce wheer we'm gooin' ter live now - they call it 'Abyssinia.!'

THE END.

THE BLACK COUNTRY SOCIETY

This voluntary society, affiliated to the Civic Trust, was founded in 1967 as a reaction to the trend of the late 1950s and early 1960s to amalgamate everything into large units and in the Midlands to sweep away the area's industrial heritage in the process.

The general aim of the Society is to create interest in the past, present and future of the Black Country, and early on it campaigned for the establishment of an industrial museum. In 1975 the Black Country Living Museum was started by Dudley Borough Council on 26 acres of totally derelict land adjoining the grounds of Dudley Castle. This has developed into an award-winning museum which attracts over 200,000 visitors annually.

In 1998 the Museum Board secured a lottery grant of nearly £3 million towards the £4.5 million cost of building a state-of-the-art interpretation centre. Known as the Rolfe Street Baths Project as it incorporated that Smethwick building which was transferred to the museum site, it was officially opened on 18 May 2001. It includes two fine exhibition halls, administration and storage rooms and retains the original Victorian building's façade. The museum's already wide range of attractions is likely soon to be increased in the field of transport with the acquisition of two major collections of vehicles.

At the Black Country Living Museum there is a boat dock fully equipped to restore narrowboats of wood and iron and different vessels can be seen on the dock throughout the year. From behind the Bottle and Glass Inn visitors can travel on a canal boat into Dudley Canal Tunnel, a memorable journey to see spectacular limestone caverns and the fascinating Castle Mill Basin.

There are over 2,650 members of the Black Country Society and all receive the quarterly magazine *The Blackcountryman,* of which 140 issues have been published since its founding in 1967. In the whole collection there are some 2,000 authoritative articles on all aspects of the Black Country by historians, teachers, researchers, students, subject experts and ordinary folk with an extraordinary story to tell. The whole constitutes a unique resource about the area and is a mine of information for students and researchers who frequently refer to it. Many schools and libraries are subscribers. Over 3,000 copies of the magazine are printed each quarter. It is non-commercial, and contributors do not receive payment for their articles.

 PO Box 71 • Kingswinford • West Midlands DY6 9YN